TAKE ᴴᴵᴹ AWAY

by

RON PIPER

To Jean
with love and hope

QUEENSPARK BOOK 29

Published by QueenSpark Books, Brighton
First Edition, November 1995

Book production by Lorraine Sitzia & John Sitzia.
Special thanks to Karen Bolton, Jean Edgar, Russell Nall, Harry
Nicholson & John Speet for help along the way.

QueenSpark Books are grateful to The Trustees of the Imperial
War Museum, London, for use of the cover photograph (IWM
D8958).

ISBN 0 904733 41 6

Printed by Delta Press, Hove, Sussex

DEDICATION

This book, although written by me, is not for me. It is for the people who gave me the will to write it. People like Jeremy Gavron, writer in residence at the Mount Prison. Without his encouragement it would not have got off the ground. However, as much as he gave me encouragement, he also criticised during the six months it took to piece it together. I, in my wisdom, and at times lack of it, both ignored and took his criticism. So to him a special thank you.

To Jean Edgar, the love of my life. It is for her that this book shaped up. For her presence in my life and the encouragement that she gave me, to her above all others I dedicate this book.

To various other people, by being part of my life, both the good and the bad, I would say many thanks. I am sure they know who they are.

A special thank you to my sister, Jean Pottinger, who over the years has stood by me with little or no return.

After completion of this book, the next thing was what to do with it. Jeremy Gavron gave his advice and I took it, sending the manuscript to QueenSpark Books at the Brighton Media Centre. Both Jeremy Gavron and the people of QueenSpark Books tell me that the copyright will still belong to me, and in the future I could still send it to 'mainstream publishers' in the hope that they may publish it too. To that I would say that QueenSpark Books are more mainstream than the mainstream, as they are at least giving me the opportunity to get into print. So I would thank them, and in particular Lorna (Jonesy) for keeping in touch, and myself informed of the book's progress.

Last but not least to Lorraine Sitzia, who went crosseyed in working so hard dotting the i's and crossing the t's in the correction of the manuscript. To her and her husband, who patiently waited for her to return to him, a very big thank you.

Also to Karen Bolton, Library Manager at Lewes Prison, and John Speet, Prison Officer, Thank You.

FOREWORD

So full of colourful characters, mischief and a sense of detachment from the horror of war, this book paints an interesting and realistic picture of how an ordinary person adapts to the hard life he is forced to live. But Rebel Ron is no ordinary person, he is the most colourful and entertaining person you could hope to meet. His warmth, sincerity and eye for comedy shine through in the story as much as in normal life.

I have to work with this guy. It is not easy, but it is never boring. His ability to tell a story - to tell it 'how it is' comes out in all different situations. I have the added advantage of having run a small branch library right in the heart of the North London area where Ron was brought up. Not a great deal has changed. The spirit and the characters live on.

I hope he writes many more absorbing novels like this one. He is an author who deserves to be noticed and enjoyed.

Karen Bolton B.A.A.L.A.
Library Manager, Lewes Prison Library Service

INTRODUCTION

I began this book and also ended it in the early part of my life, my perhaps formative years. I did this deliberately as the years after have amounted to nothing. In leaving Lewes Prison at the age of sixteen, all those years ago, I now find myself back there at the age of sixty two, finishing another term of imprisonment. The years between sixteen and sixty two have in fact been years of continuous terms of prison sentences. I do not say this with any sense of pride, but as a matter of fact. I have been told, but never bothered to count, that in total I have been sentenced to over fifty years of punishment. That of course is in total. Thank goodness for one third of that being deducted for good behaviour, otherwise I would have run out of time lived to have paid my full debt to society.

Having deliberately ended the book at the age of sixteen, I expect that some explanation of the following years should be given. As will be noted from what I have written above, those years have been spent serving prison sentences, and committing crimes that warranted, in some cases, the sentences that have been imposed upon me. I have not written of those years because they fulfilled nothing, and achieved nothing. So many books have been written on prisons and prison life, also criminal activity. In most of those that I have read, there has been a tendency to glorify crime, perhaps a Robin Hood attitude. This is far from the truth. So I have not written of those years, as looking back I can find nothing to promote. Mine has been a wasted life.

Is there any direction in which I can cast blame for those years? Perhaps there is, but to do so, words would have to be chosen very carefully. Perhaps the way of my childhood speaks and tells a story of its own, and the direction my life has taken. But blame I cast on no one but myself.

I would say to those that promote the 'flog them and hang them' attitude, think again because it does not work. I know because I have been there. Brutality whether by the system or the person cannot be anything other than retribution. It cannot and never will be a cure.

Over the years I have spent in one type of institution or another, every practice or malpractice has been carried out on myself and others like me. Various forms of punishment: the short sharp shock, diets of bread and water, solitary confinement, brute force have all been practised, all have failed. None of it has worked. For some reason or other unbeknown to me, and more to the point unbeknown to those who set the rules of the game, we have all failed together.

Better, or supposedly so, brains than mine have tried to come up with answers, but like me have been unable to do so. One thing for sure is that no form of punishment is a cure. Man being the creature he is, learns to withstand and to eventually ignore all sorts of pain.

Am I then saying that there is no cure for crime? I suppose I am. Crime has always been with us. How to deal with it is another matter. Various governments and Home Secretaries have devised all sorts of punishments and perversions in the hope that they would succeed. At the end of the day what has been their intention? I suggest it is none but a course of appeasement for the public at large and a pretence that something is being done to combat crime.

To take a man, woman, and yes, a child, put either through a system, with lack of thought, lack of ideas other than to punish, whether that system be brutal or gentle, and to turn that man, woman or child back into the world either the same or worse than when they started, isn't success; it isn't even trying.

In all the arguments that I have heard, for whatever form of punishment to be meted out to those who commit crime, I have yet to hear one that is constructive. To suggest going back to the days of flogging and hanging and so on is none other than an admission of failure, and is in no way an answer. A point that people tend to ignore is that every man, woman and child that has been placed in one sort of institution or another, has at one time been a first-timer. If any of them come back for a second, third or even fourth time, then the various systems they have been put through have failed, and so have those that set the systems. If the first-timer cannot be taught to change his or her ways then what hope is there? No system which fails at the start will succeed at the finish. Perhaps one day I will get around to writing of my adult life, but for the time being I am happy to have written of my childhood, and how it was.

In finishing this piece of my work, I live in the hope that the child be taught not by brutality, but with love. Perhaps then the adult will be more caring.

Ron Piper, 1995

at war with the Germans

SO THERE WAS A WAR GOING ON, but to me as a seven year old boy it didn't matter. People dying, being wounded, bombs falling all over London, blasting homes to the ground, it was no great fuss. What it had done for me was to fetch an excitement to my life, the bombed houses becoming dangerous playgrounds to be searched for anything that could be taken home as legitimate booty. All sorts of things were found by the gang of kids I hung around with (mainly boys, with a few girls now and again). There was money and the odd bit of jewellery which we gave to our mothers (the jewellery that is, the money we kept quiet about) but the most important find of all was shrapnel. Shrapnel was something that could be bartered with; the bigger the piece, the more that was offered by other kids who had not been so lucky in their search. A whole week's sweet ration could be asked for and got. So the hunt was on each day.

During these hunts things could become a bit macabre, especially after a night-time air raid; a night spent by whole families in the crypt of the local church, used as an air raid shelter. Emerging from the church to go back home after the all-clear had sounded, eyes were everywhere, looking for fires still burning, seeking out houses that had taken direct hits. Because as the day progressed, us kids knew we would be searching these bomb-damaged buildings for whatever could be found, to take home as our booty for the day.

So to the macabre. In our search for goods amongst the ruins, at times talk went on between us that there could be a dead body under the rubble. So the more daring of us would scour the ruins looking for a corpse. There was an awful dread inside me that one day we would uncover one. Goodness knows what would have happened if we had. I'm sure that the dead body would have been surrounded by the bodies of a gang of children who had died of fright.

One bit of bother I got into in our search for the dead went like this. With my best mate Dave, searching a bombed house we found a tailor's dummy, which we buried beneath some rubble. We then let it be known, amongst the gang of kids we got around with, that we thought we knew where there was a body. Followed by the gang we took them to our burial ground. Once there we gave them all a different spot to search, keeping our secret spot for ourselves. Pretending to dig we kept a careful eye on the others, who very reluctantly were searching amongst the rubble. Then with a shout, 'Over here!' Dave and I pointed to the ground at our feet. A deadly hush went over the ruins. Looking at the others they seemed to have a sickly look about them to me. A few of them shouted back, 'What is it?' 'A dead body,' we replied. They all took a couple of steps back and called, 'Let's call the police,' but Dave and I were having none of that, and called back, 'You're all yeller!' Gradually we coaxed them over and pointed to the dummy's hand sticking up from the ground. Little screams and gasps of shock went up around us. Bending down I grasped the hand and with a tug pulled it from the ground, and then threw it in the direction of the kids. Shouting and screaming they fled from the bomb site, leaving Dave and myself laughing, fit to bust. That is until later, when the parents of these other kids came round to our houses to complain about what we had done. They had even reported us to the police, who came round to ask us where the body was. So Dave and I had to explain what we had done. Although we got a severe warning from the local bobby, I swear I saw the glimmer of a smile on his face. After that we gave up our search for the dead, real or otherwise.

The crypt of the church I mentioned earlier was below the church that had the same name as the school we should have been attending each day, Christ Church. But no kids since then have had a better excuse not to go to school than we did. Having had our sleep disturbed by air raids during the night, we needed our sleep the following day. That is until our mums had gone to work, quite happy that we were fast asleep and safe from harm. As soon as they were out of the door, then so were we, out to the bomb sites to see what we could discover.

London at the time was full of troops from all the services, but most of them appeared to be American. Later a film was made called, 'Yanks Go Home'; at the time though I thought they were home. They seemed to be everywhere - on the streets, in the pubs and parks, in the homes of some of my friends, and even in my own home. My mother, in fact, worked as a veg cook in one of the

American services' NAAFIs, which was situated at the back of Marble Arch. Once a week my brother, sister, and I had to walk from where we lived, about a mile and a half away, to this NAAFI, and tell the soldier on guard at the door that we had come to see our mum. Once he and the other soldiers got used to us calling each week they let us in automatically and, what's more important, out again.

My mother, ever alert, knew exactly what she was doing on the days we had to meet her at work. It coincided with the day the soldiers drew their weekly rations. This was always in the mornings, so us three kids had to time our entry for the lunch time. Then we would sit, surrounded by soldiers eating, who themselves were surrounded by packages of cigarettes, sweets and toiletries. All things that, because of the war, were in short supply, but not to these American servicemen it would seem. After a while soldiers would come over to us and give us packets of sweets. They even gave us toiletries. Perhaps they thought we needed them as usually we had come straight from the bomb sites where we had been playing, and so were a scruffy-looking trio.

After all the servicemen had left the dining hall having finished their meals, my mother would come over to us, and take all the things we had been given away. She would then disappear, and after a short while would come back with everything in a carrier bag. She would then give us strict orders to go straight home, which we always did. On getting home we would unpack the carrier and share out the sweets, and then put away the tin of cornbeef, cheese, tea and whatever my mother had hidden away under our sweets. After all, who would search three scruffy kids leaving a military building, carrying sweets given to them by soldiers?

My father was away serving in the army, and until he got invalided out we saw little of him for quite a while. So discipline was at a premium, which suited us kids. My father, if anyone, was the person who had any control over my brother, sister and me. One word from him and we did exactly what we were told. With him there was no such thing as the heavy hand being at all appropriate to use on us kids, he never had the need. He had such an air about him that made his word law in our household. This applied not only to us kids but also to our mother. With my mother though, it was a completely different story. She would whack us at the drop of a hat, and not hold back with the weight of her fist or feet. Unfortunately for her (and us) it didn't work. We stood up to the beltings she gave us, where we couldn't to the look of our father.

Where we lived would today be considered a slum area, but at the time I speak of there was no such thing, or if there was no one seemed to care enough to do anything about it. With our parents, us three kids shared a three room flat in a house in a back street of St. Marylebone. A house that was shared with six other families. Our flat had one very tiny room that was my sister's bedroom, another that was my parent's bedroom, and then the one that my brother and I shared, which also did duty as our kitchen and sitting room. Trying to sleep was a virtual impossibility. My mother was a person who liked to hold court with her friends over endless cups of tea. There they would sit and gossip for hours on end, at times into the early hours of the morning.

Before my father went into the army he wouldn't stand for much of this, and somewhat tersely would tell her friends it was time for them to go, a thing he and my mother had continuous rows over. But now he was away she had her own way, and she and her friends would natter away into the small hours. I would lie beside my brother, just dozing, and listening to the gossip, not that I took much of it in, as it was all way over my head. But I would lie there listening until sheer tiredness sent me to sleep. One of my favourite things to do, as I lay there listening, was to pick at the wallpaper, as I knew that I would uncover a bug. The whole house was running alive with them. They all seemed to live just beneath the surface of the wallpaper. So there I would lie, picking away until I uncovered one. Then I would remove it to just where I wanted it to be, and then crush it under my thumb nail. I got quite a bit of satisfaction out of the small popping sound it made. I had even formed a pattern of small blotches of blood from the squashed bugs. Each night I would not be satisfied until I had squashed at least half a dozen of these lice. I had to be very careful in my hunt for bugs, as if my mother caught me I was sure to get a wallop round the head, as she always imagined that if no one disturbed the bugs that they would stay behind the wallpaper out of sight. But I knew different, as I had seen the little buggers creeping on top of the wallpaper, and not just at night. But besides fighting bugs, there was a war to be fought also, and

I, and the gang of kids I got around with, were going to do the best we could.

Of course us kids had different gangs. The one I was in was made up mainly from the street we lived in, and mostly of family as well. We had a Tarzan-like yodel or yell to call gang members together, either from home or other streets. Perhaps Tarzan got to know of our call and stole our copyright. Each gang had its own den, club, meeting place or whatever. Ours was in the basement of a house that had had a direct hit from a bomb. We had it laid out with old furniture from other ruins. Old chairs and tables, even a battered settee with the guts spewing out of it, and lit by candles we had nicked from home. And of course we put an old blanket up over the window, as it was a time of blackout, and we didn't want the ARP coming round spotting the light and kicking our arses out of our headquarters.

Anyone not in our gang was the enemy. The enemy of course being the Germans, any kid not with us was automatically a German. We were the elite, or so we thought, but kids from other gangs thought the same way. Any kid we found in our street that was not in our gang we took into custody for questioning as to what he thought he was up to. It would be put to him that he was a German spy. He would even be tortured until he confessed. To torture a spy we would tie him up in an old chair, and then gag him so that his screams could not be heard from the outside. We would pinch his nostrils together, and clasp a hand over his mouth so that he couldn't breathe. When he went red in the face we would take our hands away and ask, 'Are you going to confess?' If he didn't, we held our hands over his mouth and nostrils for longer periods, and would keep repeating the dose until the tears were streaming down his face, and he would nod yes, he was a German spy. We would then untie him and once again ask him, 'Are you a German spy?' Once he had openly admitted it, we would beat him up and send him on his way, with the strict warning that if we caught him or any of his gang of Germans on our land again, we would execute them. Of course this wasn't all one-way traffic, as if one of our gang was caught in enemy territory, then we suffered the same fate. I myself confessed to being a German spy on several occasions.

If we saw a strange adult in civilian clothes in our area, he too was a German spy. We would huddle together and whisper to each other, asking if anyone knew him. If no one did, then yes, he was a spy alright, to be followed by us to see if he would lead us to his headquarters. On one occasion we followed one man for several streets, and watched him enter a house, on which we kept watch until he left. Then we split into two groups, one to follow him, the rest to keep watch on the house to see if we could find out who else lived there. Perhaps we had found a nest of spies. The only person those of us left saw was the woman of the house, and we knew her, the bloody traitor. She was the mother of a boy in the same class as us at school. The group who had followed the spy lost contact with him when he boarded a bus. But we were not having this sort of stuff. So we planned to kidnap this boy and beat the shit out of him. If his mother was a traitor, then so was he.

We followed this kid for days on end waiting for our opportunity. Came the time, he was actually caught lurking outside our den. Now if this didn't prove that he and his mother were spies then nothing would. What if this kid was under orders to find out where our headquarters were and then tell the Germans? So we really had to torture him. The bastard just had to be spying on us and would pay for it. We pounced on him and dragged him by the scruff of the neck into our den, and then gave him the same treatment we gave all spies, plus a few whacks round the head for good measure. While the torture was going on he tried to deny that he was a traitor. But we told him what we had seen and asked, 'If you ain't a traitor, is your mother?' Now the strange thing was, he didn't deny that she was. Mind you perhaps he thought better of it, or that if his mum was a traitor, far better that she should be kidnapped and tortured for being a spy than him. So he held his silence about her. In the end we got fed up with torturing him, and gave him a good hiding and sent him home, with the threat that he and his mum had better pack up spying for the Germans, or we would really get them. There was a backlash to this. When this boy got home snivelling to his mum, she sent the police round to us. The local bobby was none too pleased with our side of the story, and he told us anymore of this sort of stuff and he would be coming around to kidnap us. It seemed the spy we had followed was none other than the woman's insurance man, calling to collect his monthly dues. But this did not deter us. We would still keep our eyes open for Germans, and deal with them in our own way.

Any male in civilian clothes and sporting a moustache was to us none other than Adolph Hitler himself. We had to be a bit crafty with Hitler, as we knew what a nutter he was. We had seen him enough times on the newsreel at the pictures, he always seemed to be shouting and hollering at people. Mind you, they didn't seem to mind, as they always appeared to be cheering, and 'Sieg Heiling' all over the place. If we came across Hitler though, in spite of our fear of him we would still follow him. We would follow him at a distance, ducking in and out of doorways if he should glance back. Of course we always lost him, as we didn't want to follow him too far in case he was leading us into a trap. After all, if we knew about him, he might well know about us. One Hitler we followed, and we must have followed many during these early war years, we decided to attack and kill. To our eyes this was definitely Adolph Hitler himself. So we surrounded him, hiding in doorways and bombed houses that he was going to have to walk past. Armed with hand grenades, of which we had an ample supply, we waited for him to draw level with us. Then giving our terrible Tarzan cry we lobbed our half-brick grenades at him. The fear of our deadly cries had rooted him to the spot, the grenades landing all around him. We didn't wait to see if we had killed him, we took to our heels, and only when we were at a safe distance did we dare to look back. We had failed, as there he stood just as we had seen him in the newsreels, shouting and waving his arms about.

Yes, we had failed to kill Hitler, but we took a gang oath to tell no one of our failure, for fear that our having failed would prolong the war. A terrible burden for us to carry, but there were still battles to be won, never lost, against the Germans. These battles went on between rival gangs. A peculiar set up altogether. When rival gangs met by accident or otherwise, the battle was on. In the gang I was in, we were the British army, but in the minds of our rivals they were too.

On an arranged battle, we would meet on neutral ground usually halfway between our different dens. Arming ourselves with our usual half-brick grenades, and rifles in the form of any piece of wood that could quickly be turned into a sword for close quarter battle, we set off to the battle ground. The usual ploy was to get there first so that we could hide ourselves amongst the rubble of the bomb site where our battles were usually fought, so that when the Germans approached we could take them by surprise, and spring out on them. If we managed this it was a complete rout, and the British army would win. There was a problem with this idea though as the Germans would try the same trick. If this happened, both sides would charge together, and both sides would be shouting, 'Come on you German bastards.' The battle would begin, each side shouting that the other side was the Germans. To any onlooker it must have appeared that German was fighting German, but the British army always won because as the losers slunk off the battle field the cry would go up from the victors, 'Piss off you German bastards, you're yeller!' This would echo round the battle field with no reply from the Germans.

After our attempt at spy catching we had to find a new den, as the kid we had tortured had told the police where the old one was and it had all been busted up. Without headquarters we were lost, but one was soon found by my brother. We had also lost all our possessions, but the place my brother had found soon cheered us up. From the outside it looked like any other house that had been boarded up because of the bombing. We pulled one of the boards from a back window and in we got, to find that the place was fully furnished with everything that we would need. We must have had the best den of all the gangs around. We soon settled in. There was a nice fireplace and plenty of fuel from the bomb sites. Once we had really established ourselves, we decided to let girls enter, a thing we had not thought of doing before. We held a meeting, and there was a lot of argument. It was decided to have a vote, and by a small majority the girls were in, which in the end suited all the boys even those who had voted against. After all, didn't the British army have women in it to act as nurses and NAAFI girls? And we were part of the army. After coming back from the battle we needed someone to tend our wounds, and also to make us tea and toast. So girls were in, and highly delighted they were too.

We were still nicking candles from home to light our den, but now we had to nick food to get our NAAFI going. Each of us was detailed to nick as much as we could, and we soon had our NAAFI up and running. Of course there were moans and groans at our houses, like, 'Who has eaten all the bread?' or 'Where's the jam or tea gone?' In our house, our mum never got a reply to any questions of that sort. It was nothing to do with us.

One of the things we enjoyed most was the weekend nights, the darker ones especially, for the following reasons. In our house there was no such thing as a babysitter, the three of us were supposed to look after each other. On Friday and Saturday nights our mum would be off to the pub, as would all the other women in the street. As soon as my mother had left the house, so did my brother and I. She would usually be out of the house by seven, and we would be on our way out by seven thirty. We would leave our sister in bed, as it seemed she could sleep through anything. If she woke while we were out, she would just turn over and go back to sleep again.

So my brother and I would be out on the streets, which was marvellous. Watching the searchlights criss-crossing the sky, flashing around amongst the stars, seeking out enemy planes. There would also be the thump of guns from nearby Hyde Park. As wonderful as it was to watch and listen to all this, it wasn't what we were out in the streets for. What we wanted was a doodlebug to come over, as one did on many occasions. The good thing about it was it could be seen and heard as it throbbed through the sky. There was a glow behind it like a light, and we could follow its course. Once spotted, we would follow it with eager eyes. Suddenly the throbbing would stop, the light would go out, and down the bomb would fall. Now we couldn't see it, but we had no fear. Although there was no way of telling where it was going to fall, we stood our ground, we had to see it through to the end. We would stand stock-still and wait, there was no way to judge distances by looking up, just wait for the roar as it hit the ground, the explosion that would follow, and the fires that would light up the night sky. The ground would tremble if the doodlebug landed anywhere near to where we lived. Then there would be people running in the direction of the explosion, shouting out to each other as to where they thought the bomb had landed. The Fire Brigade would go roaring by, the bells ringing, in the chase to douse the fires. My brother and I would follow, we just had to see it all. The excitement of it all was pretty much unbearable.

On one of our night excursions, a house near to where we lived had a direct hit, other houses around it had been reduced to rubble by the blast of the bomb. As usual my brother and I followed the stream of people running in the direction of the explosion, plus the firemen. The firemen were hardly required, as the buildings that had been damaged were hardly aflame, just the glimmer of flame here and there. Actually it was an eerie scene. After the blast there was a deathly silence. No one appeared to be talking to each other. The only sound was the sound of men and women moving rubble. Apparently it was known that people just like us had ignored the air raid alert and had stayed in their homes instead of going to the shelters. So the shifting of rubble was in fact a search for bodies. Bodies were found and stretchered off to the awaiting ambulances. I cannot remember the number of bodies that came out of those ruins, but what I do remember is that no one came out alive.

Normally my brother and I took no notice whatsoever of buildings being bombed, except as to what we could find in the debris. The most we did was to make a mental note of the house so that we could return at a later time to search for anything that could be salvaged for our den or kept for trading purposes, especially looking for shrapnel from the bomb that had caused the damage. But this night, our first night of seeing bodies removed from the ruins, was somehow different. It made the ruins seem different too, somewhere we would not go back to. We left the scene to go back to our home with not a word said between us. On arriving home we went straight to bed. Usually we were out on the streets for several hours, on this occasion we were out for not more than one. It was many nights before we dared to go back to the streets again during a night raid. Strangely we never spoke to each other about what we had seen that night, nor did we discuss our not going out at night. It just happened, that was the way it was.

But we still had our battle headquarters, and now we had girls in. We had nothing to do but plot our next battle with the Germans, whether they be young or old. Although we had nurses and NAAFI girls there was nothing soppy like kissing or any other carry on. In fact it had been made quite clear to the men that anyone caught mucking about with the girls, like kissing them, would be slung out of our army a bit lively. After all we were soldiers. The first day the NAAFI girls and nurses started we decided to have a party, so all of us had to go on the thieve at our different homes for food and drink. Having done this, and a good collection of stuff we got too, we men left the girls to prepare the feast while we went to look for any of the enemy that might be about. If we couldn't find any Germans we invented some and had mock battles, which was all good practice for the real thing when it did take place. After a couple of hours of this it was good to get back to our headquarters and the feast waiting for us. What a feast it was too, the kitchen table was full of bread and jam, biscuits and fruit. Someone had also been able to fetch a bit of luxury into our lives, as there in the centre of the table was an open tin of condensed milk for us to spread on slices of stale bread. Tea was made and the feast began. Relaxing afterwards, those of us who smoked lit up the dogends we had taken from the ashtrays at home. We were all more than pleased we had voted the girls in. They did have their uses. We men had war talk to discuss, so we banished the girls to another room. Girls in no way were to be allowed in such serious discussion. After all, girls were known to talk too much. They were none too pleased about being dismissed but they had to obey orders. Once they had left the room, and after checking the door to make sure none of them were listening, our talk began.

Eventually though our war talk was taken over by talk of girls and what they were really like. It was decided that we would look into this. Each girl was called into our war room separately and questioned about various things. They were sworn to secrecy as to what happened in our den. We told them that if they wanted to stay in our army they would each have to be examined by a doctor, or rather doctors. If any of them did not want to do this then they could leave now, but would never be allowed back. None of them refused, though there was some argument from one or two of them, when they were told that there were twelve boys in our army, and each one of them was a doctor. But we nipped that argument in the bud by telling them that they had agreed and now they must obey orders or be dismissed from our army, and that word would be put around the streets, even to the Germans, that the girls disobeying were spies, and as such should be left well alone.

So the medicals began. Each boy examined every girl thoroughly, with prodding fingers on private parts, a close examination by both hand and eye. One particular girl seemed to really enjoy the medical, she was the eldest, I guess about thirteen. Each boy took longer with her than any other. The different examinations even went further with her, fingers entered her private parts. I suppose the girls' medicals took a couple of hours. It was then time to go home, but the girls were told that further medicals might have to take place from time to time. The thirteen year old wanted to know if the girls got to examine the boys, but she was told not to be 'a dirty little cow'. Further examinations were indeed to take place.

a hap hap happy day

MONTHS SEEMED TO FLOAT BY with the usual things happening day after day. The war became a bore, but not completely so. There was still plenty for us to do but we had a lull in our operations, as it came to light that lots of us kids were to be evacuated, my brother, sister and I amongst them. We didn't want this at any price, but no matter how much we cried and pleaded with our mother it was to no avail. Then came the day, the worst day of my life so far. It seemed that all the kids, not only from our street but also from our school, were to be evacuated, and to the same place. We all had to gather at Paddington Station ready for this evacuation. Our mothers were with us, as were the teachers from our school and some people called the 'evacuating officers'. Strangely there were few tears from the gathering children; in fact, from them there was just a deep silence. The people crying were the mothers. All the kids were lined up in twos on the side of the platform at which the train we had to board was already standing. There we stood in our best clothes, with a cardboard box containing our gas masks hanging by a string around our necks. Tied in the lapel of our jackets was a label with our name and destination printed on it, and our home address. We were going to some place called Bourne End in Buckinghamshire. Standing on that platform with my brother and sister and feeling very sad, I looked around me. I could see all the other kids from the different gangs in our area. Kids that we had fought with, even the boy whose mother we had thought at one time was a traitor. She, like the rest of the mums, was crying. None of us were Germans now, nor were we going to fight each other. We were a bunch of kids full of fear for the unknown train journey ahead, unknown because none of us knew where the hell this Bourne End was. We might even be going to a foreign land.

Eventually we were all entrained. The train was a bit lopsided or should have been, as all of us were on the platform side of the train, with our faces pressed up against any available window space looking for our mums for a last farewell. There was no pushing or shoving to get in position, old enemies made room for each other. The panic was on the platform with mums pushing and shoving each other to find what window we were looking through. It was a wonder any of us could be recognised at all, our faces being so distorted by pressing so hard against the windows. With shouts of, 'Be a good boy' (or girl) echoing in our ears, a whistle blasted its tune and the train began to move off. Shouts from inside the train then began, 'Come on everybody sit down,' which with great reluctance we did. I should think that never before or since has a train full of kids been so silent.

It wasn't to be silent for long as along the aisle bounced the teachers from our school who were escorting us, giving out boiled sweets to each of us. What with sweet rationing being in force and so many boiled sweets being given out, it was a sure thing that the teachers had either nicked them or got them on the black market. After the sweets had been given out, we were told that we were now going to have a singalong. A singalong when it looked like a train full of kids at a wake! Yes, of course, it just had to be the choir master from our school that was going to lead the singing. Everyone thought he was a nutter at school when he used to stand before us at assembly with a baton in his hand, which with a tap on the music stand he would set the piano player off. Then with great movements of stick and body and the pulling of ugly faces from him, off we would have to go singing, when it was much more fun to watch his antics. Now though we knew without doubt that he was a nutter, as just for openers we all had to sing, 'It's a hap hap happy day.' Well we tried but there wasn't a 'hap hap happy' face amongst us. Unless you count the lunatic of a music teacher bouncing up and down the aisle.

Eventually we arrived at Bourne End. From the station we were formed into twos and marched off to what I later found to be the church hall. Local people walking by just stopped and stared at us struggling along with our bits and pieces of luggage, thankfully we didn't have much of that. We must have seemed a weird bunch of kids to these people, or a very well-behaved bunch of children, as there was no chatter or horse play, just an orderly crocodile of kids who didn't have the heart to muck around.

Arriving at the church hall, we filed in and were told to sit in rows on the floor. Having done this we seemed to be sitting there for hours before anything was done with us. All this time my brother, sister and I sat very close together seeking what comfort we could from each other. Eventually people began to arrive in numbers and all taking up positions in front of us. Evidently none of us were heathens, we were all Church of England. That side of things had evidently been all sorted out before we had arrived, the local vicar being one of those now standing in front of us. The vicar stepped forward and said, 'Now everybody let's have some hush,' which was a peculiar thing for him to come out with as there wasn't a sound in the place except for his voice and a muttering from the gathering of people. He was looking directly at us kids when he made this remark, but the people soon settled down. The vicar then gave a speech telling us why we were there. We were there it seemed to save us from the terrible bombing going on in London; that we would all be safe now and we would all be going to nice homes for the duration of the war. This bothered me a bit as I had no idea how long a duration was, but I hoped it would be only for a short while. He also told us that those of us that were families they would try to keep together as far as possible. Then he became all jolly in his manner and called out, 'Now girls how many of you are in the Guides or Brownies? Hands up please.' Not a hand was raised, but his eyebrows were at the lack of response, so he tried the boys. 'Well then,' he said, 'how many of the boys are in the Scouts or Cubs?' Once again no hands were raised. Now there was a sickly kind of smile on his face. I had to give him credit as he pressed on, but in a not-so-jolly voice by saying, 'Well some of you must go to Sunday school?' But again no hands were raised. So now he started to tell us that we could join any of these things if we wanted to, but we would be required to go to Sunday school. Didn't this vicar feller realise it took all our time to go to day school, without poncing about going to school on Sundays as well? I for one had no intention of going to any such place no matter what was required.

So on with the day's business. Snappily now, he called out, 'All of you stand up, boys to the left of the hall and girls to the right.' No one took a blind bit of notice of him. With this he raised his voice, 'Come on now do as you're told,' but still no one moved. Brothers and sisters wanted to stay together, not be split to the left and right. So adults moved amongst us and with a push and a shove split us up to where the vicar wanted us. Nearly all of these were ladies. Few men were around, and all these ladies sounded a bit posh to me and stank of scent. But a strange thing was now happening. These ladies now began to walk amongst us and appeared to be talking to those of us that were better dressed than the others, which did not include my brother and me. They then chose a boy or girl (and most of them appeared to choose girls), collected the chosen one's possessions, and walked with them to the front of the hall where behind a table sat a group of people who they spoke to, were given some papers and then disappeared through a doorway with the kid of their choice. For those of us left, there was terror in our hearts. What were these people doing with these kids and why weren't we being taken yet? What were they saving us for?

My sister had been taken some time before amid protestations from my brother and myself that our mother said we must stay together. It did us no good though. She was allowed to come and say goodbye to us before she was taken. The poor little cow was crying her eyes out. I felt like bloody crying too, as I know my brother did. Being a girl our sister was a bit of a pest at times, but we had got used to her and didn't mind having her around, and we were going to miss her. But I didn't cry nor did my brother. We were not going to do so in front of this posh lot. We had told our sister we would find out where they were keeping her, and not to worry, we would come and see her.

Eventually the posh lot had all gone off with the kids they had chosen, leaving behind maybe a dozen or so boys. So back on the floor we had to sit for another long wait. The only other people left were one or two official-looking characters. Finally in came another bunch of women, not so well dressed as the other mob, and no stink of perfume on them either. With this lot of women there didn't seem to be any choice of who they were going to take with them. As they passed by the table with the officials sitting behind it they were handed bundles of paper, and then approaching us called out names and off we went with them. At least my brother and I got called out together.

The lady who had been lucky enough to be given my brother and me said not one word to us, so we never spoke to her but just tagged along behind her to her house. This was situated in a narrow lane of cottages, all on one side of the lane, the other side of which was a church surrounded by a graveyard. Now I for one didn't like this situation at all, as everywhere was poorly lit and what light there was was cut out by trees and bushes, an eerie place altogether, especially to two boys brought from the streets of London with its noise, bustle and excitement. Now we were in the house of Dracula's wife. So from the moment we walked into that lane glancing fearfully in the direction of the graveyard, we decided, my brother and I, that we were not going to stay in this house.

Having entered the cottage, we were now in for a lecture on what was expected of us, how we must behave: we must wipe our feet before entering, we would go to bed at seven, our bedroom must be kept tidy at all times, we must not be rowdy in the house and lastly no friends of ours would be allowed in the house at any time. There was a few other things, like having to come straight home from school, when we would then have tea, have a wash and be ready for bed; there would be no going out at night. Little did she know that as it was winter and the nights dark, wild horses couldn't drag us out to walk past that graveyard with its strange rustlings amongst the bushes, the trees swaying and the very weird shadows that shimmered in the moonlight. So our evenings were spent in front of a wood fire just staring into the flames. The atmosphere was very strange, she sat there doing nothing, not talking to us, and we did the same not talking to her, or indeed to each other. If we did talk, we appeared to get an evil look from her that cut our conversation short. We had been given a week to get used to this new way of living before school was to start.

So our first night at this house began. At seven we were told to go to bed. We were given a candle to light our way up the stairs and to light the bedroom while we got undressed, but we were under strict orders to blow the candle out as soon as we were in bed. We slept in the same bed and very close together too. To comfort each other from the shadows in the room and from thoughts of the graveyard, we whispered to each other that we wanted to go home, and when our mother came to see us, as she had promised to do, we would beg and plead with her to take us away from this ghostly place.

That night, our first ever away from home, we cried ourselves to sleep. Gone were the brave soldiers we used to be, fighting the Germans in and around the bombsites of London. Gone too were the spycatchers. I'd even become a German myself if I could go home. We were two boys lost in the strange world of the country-side, quiet from traffic sounds, quiet except for the noise of the wind in the trees and the creaks of the old cottage we were now living in. Two frightened boys, fretting as to who this strange woman was that didn't want to talk. Were we going to be safe living with her and so close to a graveyard? No, we had never been to Sunday school, but before falling into our tearful sleep we prayed to Jesus that he would look after us during the night, and that he would look after our little sister too.

One week later we decided that there was no way we were going to stay in this house much longer. We made plans that we would do virtually the opposite to what we were told to do by this weird woman. It seemed, anyway, that we couldn't do anything right in her eyes. The slightest raising of a voice was enough to fetch her wrath upon us. A slamming door even if done accidently, an item of clothing out of place, a cup not washed up, everything we did was wrong. So sod her and her bloody orders! Deliberately we came back late from school, we argued when she said it was time for bed. If we were sent on an errand to one of the local shops, it would take us ages to come back. Of course the lady of the house called in the evacuation officer and told him she could not control us, and she wanted us out of her house. He gave us a talking to and told us we should be grateful that this lady had taken us into her home. Now that was a lot of old cobblers to me and my brother. We had been happy enough in our own home until all these evacuating people had come along and took us away. So bollocks to him! We had nothing to be grateful for. If it wasn't safe for us to live in London, then why wasn't our mum living in the country with us? If she was safe staying in London then we would be too, as she would see we were. That's how I thought of things anyway. But I didn't see the point in telling the evacuating bloke all this. In the end the lady was asked if we would be allowed to stay with her for a while longer, which she agreed, as long as it was not for too long. But we were still determined to get out of this house sooner than it looked like we were going to do. So our disruption went on.

In the kitchen of the house was a wash stand, and standing on this was a beautiful flowered wash basin and jug, both made of china. There was even a matching soap dish. This was the lady's pride and joy. It was always gleamingly clean, even after she had washed herself in it. Having finished her washing it was her habit to pick up the bowl of dirty water, go out the back door and then throw the dirty water over the grass in the back garden. Having done this she would come back into the house, wipe the bowl clean, then polish it until it was glowing with cleanliness. She would then place it back on the wash stand and then with the bowl and soap dish she would fiddle around until everything was in line, just so, even taking steps back from the stand to see how it looked, and she would not stop farting about like this until all was to her satisfaction. Of course my brother and I were never allowed to use this jug and bowl; there was an old well-chipped one for our use.

When it was time for her to have a wash, which seemed to be about ten times a day, we had to leave the room. Which we always did, but very slowly just to aggravate her. One evening she told us to leave the room as she was about to wash. On this night we did so quickly as we had a plan. Usually as soon as she had washed, and before emptying the bowl, she would pick up her dirty clothes and go to her bedroom to put fresh clothing on. On this evening she did her usual thing. Having finished washing, up she went to her room. My brother and I slipped quickly back into the kitchen, got to the wash stand and daubed thick smears of soap around the rim of the bowl. Then as quick as could be, we went back to our bedroom, the window of which looked over the back garden. Down went the lady to the kitchen, we heard the back door open and there she stood bowl in hand. With her usual toss, she hefted the bowl out in front of her to get rid of the water. Out came the water and through the air it flew in company with the bowl that had slipped through her fingers, to smash into several pieces. We jumped back from the window and onto our bed, acting all innocent, as a scream came up from below. Then there was a rush of footsteps up the stairs, our bedroom door crashed open and there she stood before us, with us lying there grinning up at her. But she just stood and stood and stood, staring at us without speaking. Gradually the grins went from our faces, our heads went down and we twitched nervously. It was spooky the way she just stood there and stared. Our nerves were gradually shattered. Finally she spoke and said, 'You wicked little bastards.'

The next day we were moved from her house and never set eyes on her again, but we did hear of her from the evacuating officer. He dressed us down; told us how ungrateful we were. Then told us that just before we moved into the lady's house, she had been told that her husband had been taken prisoner. If we had been able to collect the shattered pieces of that bowl, and put them back together again, we would have done. The thought of what we had done to this lady tamed us for a while but, being young, thoughts of her and her bowl soon left our minds.

We were moved into a new house, and although still determined to get back home we soon settled in. This house had a more cheerful atmosphere and was occupied by the lady of the house and her two daughters. The fact that it was two girls put the damper on things a bit, but after a while we got used to them, and I fell in love for the first time with the youngest daughter.

The homely atmosphere and the jolliness became a bit boring and being in love wasn't what it was cracked up to be. I didn't mind walking to school with this girl, or even going to the pictures with her on Saturday morning, but when she wanted to walk along holding my hand, that was a different matter, as I knew if I allowed that to happen all my mates would take the piss out of me. If we were on our own with no one in sight then I didn't mind too much. She even started to talk about when we were older and would I marry her, but I told her I didn't want to talk about things like that. I didn't mind at all being in love with her, but I also did not want anyone else to know, so I got her to promise to keep it a secret. Then one day we were in the house alone on our own, having a game of ludo or something, all the rest had gone shopping. I was feeling all nice sitting there with my sweetheart, playing ludo, when during a lull in the game she looked directly at me and said, 'Give me a kiss.' To say I was shocked at her asking this is to put it mildly. I didn't mind doing all the things we had been doing, like walking to school together and stuff like that, but I wasn't having any of this kissing lark, so I told her to piss off, which she did in tears. Girls really were weird. When her mother came in she told her what I had said, but not, I guess, why I said it. So I was sent to my room early that night. It was also the end of my first love affair. I promised myself in future I would be more careful with girls, as it came into my mind that if this girl was in love with me as she had said she was, she would not have snitched on me to her mother.

The end of my love affair was also the start of plans with my brother to escape back to London and normality. Of course in all this we had not forgotten our sister. When we had seen her at school soon after arriving at Bourne End, we found out where she was living and used to go to visit her. She was living in a big posh house and when we went to visit her we were not allowed in, and had to talk to her over the garden gate. On the day after my love affair broke up, it being Saturday, we called on our sister and told her we were going to escape that night, and asked if she wanted to come with us. She didn't, and really that was a relief to us both, as if she had said yes we had no idea how we would have got her out of the house where she was living. So we said our goodbyes and just spent the day idling around waiting for nightfall. It was a lovely dark night, lovely because we knew it was easier to escape in the dark. Everyone in the house we were in seemed to have the habit of going to bed early, which suited us as they were all tucked up for the night by nine thirty. But tonight we were not going to wait that long. We said goodnight to everyone at about eight o'clock, they all said goodnight back to us, that is all except my first love. She said goodnight to my brother but did not spare me so much as a glance. Still, sod her, we were escaping that night and I wouldn't be seeing her or any of them again.

We knew we were safe to leave our room any time we wished, as once we had said our goodnights no one ever came to our room to check to see if we were there. Within half an hour of being in our room we climbed out of the window and dropped into the flower bed below, where we crouched for a few moments. All was quiet, we had disturbed no one. We took to our heels, then to the station. We knew what platform to get onto for the trains to London, but first of all we had to climb a fence so as to bypass the booking office. We did this successfully. Then, hiding in the shadows, we waited patiently for the train to arrive. When it did, we dashed to it as quickly as we could. Finding an empty carriage, we hid ourselves under the seat until the train began to move. At that moment no two boys could have been happier than we were.

Soon we arrived at a station called Marlowe, and as the train was coming to a halt, back under the seats we went, and we decided that's where we would stay until we reached London. Off went the train again. Being under the seat seemed to have lost us our sense of direction as the next time it stopped, we were back at Bourne End. So once more it was back under the seats to hide, as we imagined that we had been found missing, and had been reported to the evacuating officer who had called back the train. But much to our relief after a brief stop, and no search of the train looking for us, it began to move again. Once more after a short journey the train stopped again. This time we couldn't be bothered to hide under the seats. We were just two tired boys who now didn't care what was happening, or where we ended up.

Once more the train moved, but now we had our sense of direction back. Looking out through the window we could see we were heading back from where we had come. And yes, we were soon back in Bourne End. There we wearily got off the train and, not worrying if we were caught or not, walked through the ticket office. Needless to say we were caught by the ticket collector who took us into his office where he questioned us. We gave him all our details: where we were going to, which was why we were on the train, and where we had come from and were supposed to be living. The ticket collector called the police. One copper turned up at the station. He too questioned us, again we gave our story. The ticket collector and the copper were smiling all over their faces, which was giving me the hump as I could not see anything funny about two small boys who only wanted to go home to London from this strange land, where trains didn't go anywhere except from Bourne End to Marlowe and back again. In the end the ticket collector through his laughter said, 'You won't get far on this train lads, as it's called The Marlowe Donkey, and all it does is go back and forward between these two stations.' So we were returned to where we thought we had escaped from. We didn't tell our mates what had happened to us for fear that they would take the piss, but of course they did find out, and from none other than the ex-love of my life, who couldn't put it around fast enough. A woman scorned had entered my life for the first time without my knowing it. It was a wonder to me how I could have been in love with her at all in the first place as she had such a big mouth.

Our failure did not dampen our spirits for long. In fact it made us all the more determined to get back home. Once again we went on a good behaviour strike and became little lunatics. We just would not do anything that we were told. We set off for school but did not arrive. Anything we were asked to do like tidy our room we ignored, and (sin of sins) we did not wash properly. Our necks and ears were rotten, changing clothes was forgotten. All sorts of people came to talk to us, from the evacuating officer to the vicar, but we cocked a deaf 'un to them all. Eventually we won the battle and were told one day that we had to stay in as our mother was coming to collect us. What joy we felt. She came for us in the evening and she also had our sister who she had already collected. But now she wanted to sit down and drink tea and chat to the lady of the house. Eventually we were leaving, with my brother and I out of the front door as quick as could be. As we walked away I glanced back and there was my ex-girlfriend standing on the doorstep watching us go. As I looked back, her hand came up and she began to wave goodbye, while mine came up in reply as a two-fingered gesture. As a last farewell I poked out my tongue at her. Never again, I told myself, would I fall in love. Little did I know what life had in store for me.

we ain't up to nothing

HOME AGAIN AT LAST, but to what? Things seemed to be different now. Since our departure to the quiet of Bourne End, the spirit of adventure and war games seemed to have left me. Wandering around the streets, not meeting too many other kids (most of them still being at Bourne End or some other such outlandish place), things definitely were not the same.

I went round to look at what used to be our fully-furnished den, only to find a little old lady was living there. As I was to find out later, it was her home and had only been boarded up for safety, as it seems she too had been evacuated and like us had not liked it, and so had come back to her home. So somehow she had escaped too. I wonder if she had had the same problems as my brother and I, and what she must have felt, that coming home after her escape she found that someone had been living in her house. Perhaps she had even wondered if it had been a German spy. There was no going around to find another den, or to form another army, or even going round to scour the ruins looking for shrapnel or other loot. Part of my life was finished. I was now getting on for ten and felt grown up, not for me any more kids' games. Even the Germans seemed to have lost interest as the air raid warnings seemed to sound less and less. When they did, there was not the same excitement, the bombs did not fall so often. Even where I lived seemed to have changed, the bomb sites had been tidied up. But I had to do something, so I began to attend school regularly, just out of boredom. I met up with my old mate Dave again, he hadn't been evacuated at all. The pair of us mooched around the streets, tossing the odd brick or two through windows that had stood up to bomb blast. Now and again we threw bricks through windows of houses that we thought were empty, only to get a volley of abuse from people who were still living there. We just had to get into something and we did, and something that was to earn us a few bob too.

People were always looking around for things for their homes, especially if their first homes had been damaged in an air raid or ruined altogether. They wanted furniture, pots, pans, anything to build a new home with. What I couldn't make out was that with all the bombed houses there were around, with some perfectly good furniture in parts of them, and no one living there, why they just didn't go along and pick it up and cart it off back home. A couple of people who were moaning about wanting this and that, I told where they could pick up the stuff that they wanted. But I was told by them that they couldn't do that as it was looting. Now I had never heard of this looting lark and couldn't see the problem. So I asked my mum and she said yes, it was looting to go taking things from bombed houses, and the police and air raid wardens were keeping their eyes out for people doing it, and anyone caught looting could be shot on sight. Now whether she told me this to frighten me off, I don't know, but I did know she didn't succeed, as with my mate Dave I took to looting. Looting became our game and the fear of getting shot on sight if we were caught brought the excitement back into our lives. So we kept our ears open for anyone passing the comment that they needed tables, chairs, or anything else for their homes, and then we would let them know that we could get it. Of course, not being stupid, we always asked how much they would give us for whatever it was they wanted. A shilling, a tanner and even a couple of pennies would be quoted to us according to what was required. Then we would set off on our looting raids.

Of course it all had to be done with great stealth, even going as far as to dirty our faces so that only the whites of our eyes showed. After all we didn't want to get shot if we could avoid it. Strangely enough, although the women who bought the stuff from us must have known that our lives were at risk, none of them warned us as to the danger. Not that we would have taken any notice as it was a good business, and Dave and I always had a couple of bob in our pockets to buy black market sweets with, from the shop just round the corner from where we lived. We had even thought of going into the black market ourselves but we didn't know where the market was that all these shopkeepers were buying the stuff from, and they wouldn't tell us. We did ask quite a few of them about it, but all they did was to wink at us and start to laugh. Even if we could have found out, we didn't know if two or three shillings would set us up. So we decided to stick to looting.

Looting of course had to be done after dark. The loot carried through the dark streets, all the time keeping an eye out for the police and wardens. It was a risky business; at times we had to make several trips to get all the stuff we had on order. Getting it wasn't the problem, it was getting it to the people that had ordered it and then getting our money. One woman we got some chairs for kept putting off paying us saying, 'I can't afford it this week,' and so on. After a couple of weeks of this we got the hump with her. One Saturday night we watched her leave for the pub. Then breaking a window in her house we got in and nicked the stuff back, plus one or two other pieces as well. After that we avoided that woman like the plague.

But then came the time that put us off looting for a while, as there we were in the basement of a house that had been boarded up for safety and which we entered by taking one of the boards from a window at the back, our usual ploy. Oddly enough this was not a looting expedition but a scouting one, which we were always doing so that we would know just where we could get things for any orders that we might get. Anyway, there we were in this basement, quite happily shining our torches on bits and pieces that at sometime could be sold, when from another room further along the passage came a call, 'Is anybody there?'

We froze, we shook, we gasped. 'Who the hell is that?' I whispered to Dave, but got no reply from him. He just stood there mouth agape.

Then footsteps were to be heard coming along the passage, the voice still calling, 'Is there anybody there?' As if of one accord we both moved as silently as we could in the dark (we had switched our torches off at the first call) in the direction of a cupboard in the corner of the room, which we got into and pulled the door behind us. I was shaking like a leaf, as was Dave beside me. I was praying to whatever gods there were, 'Please don't let him shoot me, I won't go looting anymore.' But still the footsteps came on. They were in the same room we were, a torch was flashing here and there. Peering through a crack in the door, I could see the flickering shadows cast by his torchlight.

Dave whispered to me, 'He's got a gun.'

The footsteps were nearing our cupboard. Screaming at the top of our voices, 'Don't shoot!' we flew out of the cupboard down the passage and out of the window to freedom. Behind us we had left a screaming terrified tramp who we later found out had been living in the basement. It wasn't until some time later that we found this out, and, as I've said, it put us off looting for a while. But only until we heard who it was, and that he was more terrified than we were when two black apparitions came at him like bats out of hell from the cupboard. We were not prepared to risk getting shot for at least a week, which is when we found it was just a tramp. Once we had learnt of this it was business as usual.

There was however to be another slight hitch to our looting, even if just a stutter. My father, who had been in the army, had been invalided out for a few weeks now, and he had joined the ARP to act as a warden during air raids, still determined to do his bit for the war effort. He only lived with us for a short while, and then he and my mother split up. My father was the black sheep of the family as he wouldn't nick a thing, while the rest of us would. During his duty as a warden, he went to a house that had bomb damage done to it during a raid. While searching for any injured, he came across a box that was full of sovereigns and half sovereigns. He made the mistake of fetching them to our house before handing them in at his warden post. When my mother heard what he intended to do, she went absolutely spare and a terrible row took place. But none the less for that he still handed them in. Rumour then had it that that was the reason why they parted, my father being too honest, although I had my doubts about that theory. They were to never live together again.

All that though is by the way. What concerned Dave and myself was that my father, now being a warden, would be roaming the streets at night while we were out looting. With that thought also came the thought that if he would shoot me if he caught me and Dave red-handed. So we now had to be extra vigilant as I didn't fancy being shot by my own father; it wouldn't seem right somehow.

There was one other problem: my brother also wanted to join us at looting but neither Dave or myself liked his mate. At one time he had been in one of the opposing gangs, and what's more the leader too. We explained this to my brother, in spite of the fact that he knew it anyway, but, blood being thicker than water, we said yes, he could join us, but first he had to get rid of his mate. As my brother had been friends with this kid for a while he didn't just want to tell him that he wasn't going to be his friend anymore, and that he was going to go with Dave and me. But get rid of this kid we had to do. So it was left to Dave and I to do it. Then at a later stage my brother could say it wasn't his fault and maybe become friends with this kid again. Although to my knowledge they never did. Which is not surprising with what Dave and I had planned for this kid.

Dave and I hatched several plots to get rid of this kid but cast them all aside. Why the hell the two of us didn't just beat him up and tell him to fuck off I don't know, unless it was the fact that he was a lot bigger than us. One plot we did give a lot of thought to was this; to let him come on a looting raid with us but making sure there were wardens nearby. Then while looting, kick up such a row that it was sure to fetch them down on us. The plan being that as Dave and I knew what would happen, this kid wouldn't, so we would make a quick getaway, while he being slow off the mark would be caught and shot. We even thought of luring him into a bombed house we knew, and pushing him into a hole and hoping he would break a leg or some other limb. All sorts of accidents we planned but they all seemed a bit drastic, even to us.

So entered the thirteen year old girl who I've mentioned earlier. She would drop her knickers for any boy to have a feel or a look providing he had a sweet or two to give her. My brother's mate was always on about girls, or 'tarts' as we called them then. So we told him that this tart we knew would let him have a look and feel if he gave her a toffee bar or whatever. He jumped at this offer straight away. As he didn't know her, Dave and I made arrangements to meet this girl in one of the ruins. We told her there would be four of us, which she didn't mind at all. She was there for the meeting, waiting and ready, eager to get on with things before my brother, Dave, this other boy and myself arrived. Of course my brother was in on the plot. We all sat around in a circle chatting when this girl let it be known that she wasn't going to show the four of us in one go. No doubt she thought that if she did we would try to get away with giving her just the one toffee bar. This was our cue. We told her only this kid wanted to see and feel her as we had already done so when we had given her the medical when she had joined our army as a NAAFI girl. So off we went, Dave, my brother and I, leaving the pair of them alone. We rushed straight round to the girl's house and knocked on the door. When her mother opened it we all shouted together, 'Oi missis! Some kid's got your Molly's knickers down in those ruins over there,' pointing out the exact location. Off flew the girl's mother and caught them bang at it with the boy looking closely at the knickerless girl. Once the mum had seen what was going on there was hell to pay. Plenty of f-ing and blinding, and the sound of someone being walloped. The boy came out of the building so fast, it was as if he was being shot at by the wardens. The girl, well she got dragged off home by her earhole. But it did the trick, all this kid did after that was to skulk around corners trying to make sure no one saw him. Of course we had told as many kids as we could, without telling them the part we had played. For months after that any of the kids who saw this boy would call out after him, 'Little Tommy Tucker is a dirty little fucker!'

There was a tail-end to this story. The girl's mother never told her how she found out what she was doing, so she had no idea that we had set her up. Which was a good thing as we wanted to keep in with her as we never knew when we would fancy a look or feel ourselves.

So our looting went on, and it was quite a prosperous business for the three of us. But there was another sideline to come that proved to be a bigger earner for us. Before that got off the ground though, we once again fell foul of the law. Not too far from where we lived was a sort of park called Paddington Recreation Ground. One day us three looters decided to take a day off, and take a rest from our toils by paying a visit to this park, and to see who we could aggravate there. On arriving we were disappointed to find that there were not too many people about except for the odd elderly couple here and there. So we mooched about, swinging off a few trees, just aimless wandering really. We were beginning to get the hump with ourselves for ever coming over to this place, and were talking about going back to our own area. It was then that we noticed about half a dozen great mounds of earth, all grassed over and all of them appeared to be the same shape. We decided to investigate these mounds, only to find that in the side of each of them was a padlocked door. On each door was a notice saying 'DANGER - KEEP OUT'. Now whoever put those notices up had to be right off his nut. As far as us kids were concerned it would have been far better to have put up notices saying, 'Welcome please enter'. That type of notice would have stood more chance of keeping us out. As it stood though Dave, my brother and I attacked the padlock on one of the doors and soon had the place opened up. Swinging the door open we were greeted by total darkness. Of course none of us was afraid of the dark as we were so used to roaming the streets at night, and our looting was also done at night, but then we at least had our torches with us. This was a different dark. We couldn't see a bloody thing, and, as brave as we all were, there was no way we were going to enter this dungeon. So it meant a quick sortie to the local shop to buy a box of matches and then back again. Striking a match about six foot from the door we approached the gloom. By the time we had reached the door the match had gone out as did another dozen or so. None of us actually wanted to go in and then strike a match.

Eventually Dave screwed up his courage and said he would do it. My brother and I gave him our full support from a good distance away. Within a few seconds of his entering, out of the flickering shadows of matchlight came Dave's voice. 'Gawd almighty,' he yelled.

Taking a couple of quick steps backwards, and in unison, my brother and I called back, 'What's in there?'

'Bombs' came the reply.

Bombs! We were in there like a shot, striking matches all over the place, and there they were, racks and racks of bombs. What a find this was. Of course our days of hunting shrapnel were over, but a bomb, this was different. No kid we knew had ever had a whole bomb. In the end we wrestled one of the bombs from the racking it was on and took it outside. It was a bit of a disappointment as it wasn't very big. We inspected it fully, and experts that we were, agreed that it was intact. There we were with this bomb, and bombs went off with a bloody big bang. We wrestled it to the top of the mound we had got it from. Once there, the three of us rested for a while. After recovering from our exertions lifting the bomb between the three of us, we heaved it over the side of the mound to the ground some twelve feet below. Imagine our disappointment when there was no explosion, but just a dull thud as it hit the ground. We were to try doing this several times, still no success.

An old couple who had stood watching us for a moment or two shouted up to us, 'What do you think you're doing?'

'Trying to set this bloody bomb off,' was our reply, as once more we threw it to the ground below. Well I don't know how old this couple were, but they looked pretty ancient to me. As the bomb hurtled to the ground, without a backward glance, they left the vicinity faster than two two-year-old fillies.

We soon got tired of this carry on and decided to take the bomb home. That really was a struggle and seemed to take hours. Eventually we arrived and carted the bomb into our kitchen, and with a great thud plonked it on the kitchen table. My mother, who was in her bedroom, shouted out, 'Is that you kids? What are you up to?'

We called back, 'Yes it's us mum, we ain't up to nothing, we just fetched a bomb home.'

There was a sort of screech from the bedroom and my mother's face appeared round the door. Seeing that we were telling the truth for once did us no favours with her, as now the screeching turned into full scale screams of, 'Get the fucking thing out of here.' Her face seemed to be a funny colour to me, it was blue, but I hardly had time to think about what she had been doing to herself, when with more shouting of, 'Get the bloody thing out of here,' she flew out of the bedroom and whack, whack, whack, the three of us got a clump round the head followed by more screams of, 'Get it out and back to where you got it.' It was no good our protesting, so manhandling the bomb back out again we were followed by the shout, 'And if the bloody bomb don't kill yer, I will when you get back!'

There was no way we were going to take the bomb all the way back again. We decided to dump it on the corner of the street and that would be that. Just as we had put it down, round the corner came this large copper. We were just about to run off when he shouted, 'Oi you three stay there.' We froze, there being no point in our running, as he knew us anyway.

'What's all this then?' he asked.

'A bomb,' we chirped back to him.

Looking down and seeing that what we said was true, he took five or six rapid paces back and began to start blowing his whistle like mad. Suddenly we were surrounded by a crowd of people, including another couple of coppers, but they all appeared to be giving us a wide berth. We stood virtually on top of the bomb, while they stood yards away. They jumped back even further when Dave idly gave the bomb a kick, one of the coppers shouting, 'Leave the fucking thing alone you little bastards!' I think I was more surprised at hearing him swear than if the bomb had gone off.

Eventually we were carted off to the police station where in the end we told them where the bomb had come from. We wound up getting nicked for breaking into the place, and nicking the bomb, and had to go to court. In the court we had to sit on chairs facing three old ladies sitting behind a large table, with our mothers on chairs behind us. Of course we admitted nicking the bomb. The copper who caught us told the magistrates the whys and wherefores of the case. Then the old girl sitting in the middle gave the three of us a lecture along the lines of, 'Didn't we know how dangerous it was, the bomb could go off,' on and on she went. Of course we knew the bomb could have gone off, hadn't we spent half the afternoon knackering ourselves trying to make it do just that. In the end she gave the three of us a very severe warning; not to get into any more trouble or she would send us away. Sod that I thought. We would have to be very careful or she would have us evacuated again, the old prat.

I mentioned earlier about another business opening that was to come our way. This was to turn us into metal dealers, as it seemed that lead was in great demand. As we lived in a tenement house surrounded by rows of other such like houses, and all of them being supplied by cold water only fed through lead pipes, there was an abundance of that particular metal around, and easy to come by from the bomb-damaged houses.

Living in a cold-water flat made it a bit of a chore to have a hot bath. The water had to be boiled on the gas stove and then poured into a large zinc bath (a thing every household had) and usually set up in the middle of the kitchen floor. To empty this was a chore in itself. The three rooms we lived in were on the second floor of the house. If anyone had a bath, then to empty the water we would open the kitchen window (always at the back of the house and looking over the backyards), manhandle the bath onto the window sill, and slowly tilt it until the water began to flow down to the yard. Except for some soldiers, most of them being American, there were few young men about, so most of the bathing was done by women. On Friday and Saturday nights the falling of water into the backyards was like a gigantic waterfall the length of the street, as all the women were poncing themselves up ready for a night up the pub.

In the week, if a bath full of water was tipped anywhere near us, my mother would comment to any of her cronies in the house, 'Her next door is going out again, wait until her old man hears about it. He will murder her!' Why the hell her old man would murder her because she had a bath and was going out put me at a complete loss. It was only when I heard gossip that Mrs So and so was 'having it with a Yank' that I began to understand. Even then, what the hell she was 'having with a Yank' still puzzled me. But if we saw any of these women's kids in the streets we shouted after them, 'Your mum's having it with a Yank.' I remember it was shouted after me once, and when I got home later I said to my mum, 'Mum are you having it with a Yank?' For which I got a quick but very sharp smack in the mouth. I never asked that question again. Whatever this 'having it with a Yank' was had to be something bad, or something secret for the war effort that shouldn't be talked about.

Anyway back to lead. We had come across a bloke who told us kids that if we came across any lead in the ruins he would give us money for it. Well there was tons of the stuff about, which is why we gave up looting (at least full time) and took to dealing in metal. Once again we would wait until it was dark before setting out to gather lead, just as we did with looting. The three of us, that is, Dave, my brother and myself, carried a sack and a torch each, as our working gear. It was hard work as some of the lead had to be pulled off the wall and twisted until it snapped. Once we had got as much as we could carry, we would head off to the bloke who wanted to buy it. We couldn't carry too much of it, it being so heavy, but we were getting some every evening. Through our nights of looting we knew just where to go, as time after time we had seen lead, but had not given it a second thought. Although it was hard work it paid better than looting, which was dropping off as a business anyway as people seemed to want less and less pots and pans and furniture. Occasionally we were asked to get something or other and we never refused as it was money for old rope anyway. Nicking lead though was now our main money getter. The three of us always had plenty of money. It was nothing for me to have a couple of pounds tied up in an old rag that I used as a snot rag. This old rag with the money in it used to go to bed with me, as a couple of times when my mother thought that my brother and I were asleep, I watched her going through our pockets, and on at least one occasion she nicked a bit of money off of me. After that time I was more cagey.

To make our lead-nicking easier, we each armed ourselves with a chopper. We could now work twice as fast and even go into the bombed houses during the day to hack the lead down ready for collecting. We would still not cart it off until it was dark though. One Friday evening we set off quite early to do the business. We didn't have far to go as in a bombed house in the street where we lived we had spotted the biggest lead pipe we had come across. It was our intention to hack this down and sack it up ready for carting off the next night. Getting into the basement of this house where this pipe was was easy. Once in, there was the lead pipe running the width of one room and also up the wall from floor to ceiling. Taking a spot each we started to hack away together. Suddenly there was water everywhere soaking us to the skin. Jumping back startled at this in the first place, we looked at each other and then began laughing. As we were already soaked through we decided to carry on as it was a sure thing that we couldn't get any wetter. Having completed our work we planned to go home and get some dry clothes on, and then go to the pictures for the evening show. On emerging into the street we quickly changed our minds about going home, for a while at least, as going along the street to our house it seemed as if every woman in the street was looking out their window and all shouting, and as it was a time of blackout still, it was all the more surprising.

The whole street was lit up as if war had ended or something. All these women were shouting, 'Whose turned the fucking water off?' Other comments were flying around such as, 'How can I have a bath? I'm supposed to be at the pub at seven.' Strolling along casually taking no notice of all this shouting, we looked at each other and began to laugh once more. We didn't go home as we did not want our mother to see us soaking wet as she was one of the women shouting out the window. So we had to wait until she went to the pub before going indoors. Not being able to wash did not, in the end, stop any of the women going out. We three though spent an uncomfortable half an hour or so on the street corner in our wet clothes. By the time we could get safely indoors it was too late for the pictures. The next day workmen came round to the bombed house where our pipe was and repaired it. They also took away the lead we had cut down, the thieving bastards!

Although we were working and earning quite a bit of money we still had to go to school. With the bombing becoming less frequent, the old excuse of being too tired had now worn thin. If we didn't go to school and 'hopped the wag' (as it was called) and the local copper caught us roaming the streets, there was hell to pay. He would even threaten us with being locked up. This sort of talk put the frighteners on us for a while as we were never told where he would lock us up, and not knowing that was a lot more frightening than the threat for some reason or other. I reckon we must have had visions of some dark dungeon somewhere, but that threat soon wore off. Even the threat of being locked up couldn't get us to school every day. We just had to keep a watchful eye out for the copper on the many days that we did hop the wag. We skulked around the streets looking, I should think, very suspicious. In our spy-catching days, if we had seen anyone skulking around like we were now doing we most certainly would have put them down as spies and dealt with them accordingly. It was actually becoming quite a feat to hop the wag, as besides the copper we also had to avoid bumping into our mum who would give us a hiding if she caught us. Gawd knows what had got into her as she never use to bother too much if we didn't go to school, but now she was becoming worse than the copper.

There was one day of the week that all the kids hated to go to school on. That was the day that Nitty Nora was to be there. She was a crafty cow as she tumbled why the school was three quarters empty when she appeared. So to catch us all out she began to show up on any old day. But the school spy system soon found out what she was up to, and word would go round saying, 'Nitty Nora is in tomorrow.' So we all hopped the wag the following day as this woman was a pest. One at a time she would call us into the room set aside for her, and go through our hair with a fine tooth comb (and she was none too gentle with the comb) looking for nits and fleas. These she found in their hundreds, all the school was lousy. As fast as she could clear them up, back they came again.

As we were all lousy there was no shame in being so. The thing we didn't like was being sent to the clinic. Any kid found to be lousy was given a letter to take home to their mothers telling her to take them to the clinic to get deloused. For some reason or other everyone called the clinic 'The Bake'; to this day I do not know why. The reason no one liked going there was that on arrival the lousy one would be greeted by another Nitty Nora. You would then be taken to a bathroom and made to take off all your clothes, and then stand naked in the empty bath. Once you were in there, along would come Nitty Nora with a paint brush and a bucket full of evil smelling liquid. Dipping the brush into this liquid, she would then paint the whole of the kid's body, and be none too gentle in doing so, which could be a bit painful, especially when she went slap, slap, slap with the brush round your balls. As I've said, the stuff she slapped on with this paint brush was evil smelling, and the smell lingered for days afterwards no matter how hard you may have tried to wash it off.

But it came about that being lousy was to become a bonus. If you got sent to The Bake, you got the day off school. Now the kids, once they became aware of this, wanted to go to school on the day that Nitty Nora was due, but of course you had to be lousy. If by some misfortune you were not, it was the thing to find someone who was and get a few fleas off of their head, put them on your own and hope that that did the trick. After a session at The Bake, and now having the day off school, we could wander around the streets at will with no fear of being locked up by the copper. However, if he saw you in the streets he would still stop you and ask, 'Why aren't you at school?' But now he could be looked right in the eye and told, 'I'm lousy, ain't I,' a thing that he never queried. In fact he couldn't move away fast enough, fearing, I suppose, one of our fleas leaping on him. On the few occasions that I was not lousy and hopped the wag, I used that excuse, as did Dave and my brother. It was an excuse that was never questioned. Looking back now I wonder why I never tumbled to the fact that I could have got a good living by selling fleas to kids that were not lousy and who wanted a day off school. I'm sure it would have been a thriving business as there was never a shortage of stock. But lousy or not we still had our business to run. The metal dealing was still our best earner, but we were soon to branch out further and into a much more serious game.

doing Chocolate Joe's

JUST ROUND THE CORNER FROM WHERE WE LIVED, in a street called Church Street, was a shop called Chocolate Joe's, the name also given to the owner of the shop. He sold nothing other than sweets of every variety. His shop window was just one glorious display of sweets from sherbert to boxes of chocolate. How he managed this no one could fathom out. Most other sweet shops had just a small display and not much choice. Once a week we were given our week's sweet coupons by our mother with a couple of pennies. Armed with this we would then go to the sweet shop of our choice, strangely enough never to Chocolate Joe's. We went to a ramshackle old shop on the corner of our street run by an old feller everyone called Guv. We had learnt that he was the best one to deal with as, unlike Chocolate Joe, he wasn't stingy with his weighing of the sweets. Another thing in his favour (ours depending on how you looked at it) was when we had no coupons he would let us buy a few sweets without coupons, but over the odds with the price. Guv also had a wonderful collection of comics. We could go into his shop and change old comics for ones we had not read, and he always had such a selection that there was a comic of one sort or the other that could be swapped. How and why he did this I don't really know as no money ever changed hands, just one comic for another.

Anyway, back to the new business, and this concerned Chocolate Joe. Now Chocolate Joe did not live above his shop like most other shopkeepers did. When he had finished his day's work, he simply locked up for the night and went home wherever. So our next business was to get into his shop at night and nick as many of his sweets as we could. The way we had it worked out was to wait for an air raid (when most people would be either in their houses or the air raid shelters) and then attack the shop. We had to wait for an early evening raid as we could hardly get out in the early hours of the morning. The best time, of course, for us would be for the Germans to come over and start bombing on a Friday or Saturday night. Then everyone would be in the pub and, as our mum would be too, we would have longer on the streets. So we settled on a weekend to get into Chocolate Joe's. There was no particular hurry as we were still nicking plenty of lead, but the weekends came and went without opportunity. What were these bloody Germans up to? Why couldn't they fly over and drop a few bombs? The usual trio of Dave, my brother and me were not going to give up on this. If the Germans didn't come soon we would do Chocolate Joe's anyway.

As each day passed we walked past Joe's, our mouths watering, getting the hump more and more with the German air force. There were one or two day-time alerts but that was no good to us. Then came the night we had waited for, the sirens sounded and yes, on a weekend night too. So off the three of us went to Chocolate Joe's. We each had a sack with us, ones we used for collecting lead, and Dave had a house brick. The only lights that were visible were the searchlights moving around the sky looking for enemy planes. We waited in a doorway near to the shop, waiting for the guns in Hyde Park to start banging off, hoping that one of the German planes would drop a bomb somewhere near to us. But please God not on Chocolate Joe's! But there was just a deathly silence, not even the drone of a plane. Now we decided to get on with it anyway as there was no one about.

In front of Joe's, my brother took the brick from Dave. Then, standing in front of Joe's window, he took an almighty swing and lobbed the brick at it, and straight through it went. With a crash loud enough to wake the dead, the window crashed to the ground in a thousand pieces. I must admit that the noise it made frightened the bloody life out of me. We waited a short while to see if the noise had attracted anyone; it hadn't. So into the window we went and loaded up our sacks with every sort of sweet we could lay our hands on. When our sacks were full we staggered home with our load. We had enough sweets to last us no matter how long the war was to go on for.

As we staggered home I could actually taste the chocolate in my mouth. Arriving home we tipped our sack of sweets onto the floor. A more colourful display no one in the world could ever have seen before. Sweet wrappers of every shade glittered in the gas light. Then with one accord we reached out with tentative hands and took a sweet each, we did not want to disturb this beautiful sight. Having picked a sweet each, we quickly unwrapped them and popped them into our mouths. Just as quickly we spat them out again, they tasted vile. Quickly we looked through this pile of sweets now, not caring about disturbing them, as each of us knew in our minds, without one telling the other, that all our lovely sweets were dummies. We were so angry with Chocolate Joe, for so long now he had been tempting us with this display of dummy sweets. We were determined to get our revenge on him, one way or the other.

Before that though there was one other person we wanted to take down a peg or two, this person being an ARP warden called Big and Ugly. Everyone called him that, even the adults, and that's exactly what he was. It seemed to us kids that besides his being a warden, his job was also to aggravate us. No matter what we were doing, to him it was wrong. If we were just standing on the street corner talking, he made us move on. If we played football in the street he stopped us. Even our parents got fed up with him and had rows with him over us kids, telling him to leave us alone. But not him, he was just one very officious man. The tin helmet he wore on his head, with ARP painted on it, went to his head in more ways than one. But how to get our own back on him? That was the problem. We had thought of climbing onto bombed houses, and as he rode by on his bike pelting him with bricks. We gave up on that idea, his wearing a tin helmet put us off of that as there was no way we could split his head open while he had that on, and we could think of no way that we could get him to take it off while we threw bricks at him. In fact since he had joined the ARP no one had ever seen him with the helmet off. We puzzled our heads for days over this. Big and Ugly was a ferocious looking man and put the fear of God in us kids. If he shouted at us he could be heard streets away. We had to get him, so with great trepidation we set off on the course that we hoped would quieten him down.

The plan was to catch him as he rode his bike around the streets, as he did both day and night. For our plan to succeed it had to be carried out at night for two reasons: one so that he could not tumble to our plan; secondly, and far more important, so that he couldn't see us as we carried the plan out. The thought of him maybe doing just that nearly put us off the plan. In a street called Bell Street were two lamp posts directly opposite each other, because of blackout restrictions they were never alight. With the usual three of us (Dave, my brother and myself) the plan was carried out one dark night. We tied a rope to one lamp post, and draping it loosely across the road and round the lamp post opposite, we hid in a nearby doorway and waited for him to come riding along, which eventually he did. Watching the lamp on the front of his bike we quickly pulled the rope taut between the two lamp posts, securing the loose end. The rope was now two feet off of the ground, our trap was laid. Along came Big and Ugly straight into the rope and flying head over heels into the road, his bike collapsing on top of him. For a minute or two he laid there stunned, then shakily stood up holding his head. He drew himself up to his full height. But what was this? This wasn't Big and Ugly. It was another warden that we didn't know, and only a small man at that. We never did find out who this man was. Disconsolately we watched him untie the rope, roll it up and with his bike walk away into the dusk rubbing his head. We had failed to get Big and Ugly, but were now more intent on getting him than ever. Our revenge list had now gone up to two in number: Big and Ugly and Chocolate Joe.

Around this time things seemed to be slowing up, not from the point of view of our business (looting and nicking lead were still earning us money) but there didn't seem to be as many American soldiers around. There was a quieter atmosphere in the pubs. Rumour had it that the war was nearly over. A rumour that Dave, my brother and I hoped was not true; we didn't want the war to end just yet. In the meantime we carried on as usual. On weekend nights we started to hang around outside the pubs, waiting for the Yanks to come out drunk at closing time as they were then an easier touch than they were sober. The Hackneyed phrase of 'got any gum chum' was well used by us three, but using it outside a pub at closing time didn't yield much gum; it did better than that, it got us hands full of loose change from the Yanks, which suited us fine. I'd had so much gum during this war it was coming out of my ears. If anyone had looked behind my ears at this period of time they would have thought that that was true, as there was always a bit of gum stuck behind my earhole, where it was put for safekeeping for the next time I wanted a chew at it.

There seemed at this time to be a lot of parties going on in homes, not just in our street but all around. These usually took place on Saturday nights. Bottles of beer would be fetched back from the pubs, a couple of bottles of spirits also if you were in good with the landlord, as that, like most things, was in short supply. The Yanks always fetched a bottle or two along, they never seemed to be short of anything. There were many parties at our house. I'd never had a drink of beer or spirits, but I was determined to do so one day as from what I could see of it it made everybody happy, for a few hours anyway. As in the pubs, at parties there was singing and dancing. People would sing 'White Cliffs of Dover' and 'When The Lights Go On All Over The World'. The one that got everyone going was 'Knees Up Mother Brown'; 'knees up, knees up, don't get the breeze up, knees up Mother Brown!' Even the soldiers used to pull their trouser legs up to their knees and leap everywhere; a peculiar sight, but us kids enjoyed it as we were allowed to stay up if a party was held in our house. Not that we could have got any sleep if we had been made to go to bed, what with all the noise. At party time we always collected money from the Yanks or whoever was there. There was always plenty of fags laying around, and being smokers my brother and I would nick as many of them as we could. Many a time in the early hours of the morning someone would shout out, 'Anyone got a fag?' We had, but we cocked a deaf 'un to this cry. But our mum would say, 'My Ron and John have.' People would come over and ask us for a fag, but still we denied having any. But they would keep pestering us until in the end we said we would sell them one.

We used to get some dirty looks off of some of them as quite a few of those asking for fags had already given us money. But if they wanted a fag bad enough they would pay. We had stashed the fags we nicked out on the landing so we would have to go out there before we made a sale, being careful that we were not followed by anyone who might nick our stash. The Yanks especially used to give us old-fashioned looks when we sold them a Lucky Strike or a Camel, their own brand of fag. Every time we made a sale our mother used to head in our direction, smiling all over her face, and for some reason give us a big wet sloppy kiss, which we hated in front of all those people. There was many a morning when we woke up without a fag ourselves, having sold all those we had nicked from the people back to them.

Then came the day we got our revenge on Big and Ugly. Although we didn't get to know the full result of what he had to say about what we did to him, it did not leave a lot to the imagination. Walking along one evening we saw his bike leaning up against a wall with him nowhere in sight. At first we thought of smashing it up, but then my brother noticed some dog shit on the pavement. Scooping this up we spread it all over his saddle, as thick as we could, then smeared some thinly on the underside of the handle bars, and retired to a shop doorway on the other side of the road to wait and watch. As he came back, we began to shout and push each other about to distract him. It worked a treat. He got excited and as usual started to shout at us, 'Get out of it,' as he headed in our direction. One of us shouted out, 'Bollocks!' and then the three of us hared off down the road, with him leaping onto his bike to peddle as fast as he could after us, which is just what we wanted. We left him far behind, as we took off across the bombsites where he couldn't follow on his bike. Revenge on Big and Ugly was smelly and sweet, but we still had to get back at Chocolate Joe. Big and Ugly was tamed, he was never seen to ride his bike again around our streets. He seemed also to have lost his voice; still as ferocious looking, but very quiet!

Back to our nicking lead. What we had been doing was to work at it daily. We were also building a stockpile in one of the rooms of a bombed house, as we were chopping down far more than we could carry each day to our buyer. We had amassed so much lead now that we decided to stop for a while, and just sell off what we had bit by bit. Then when the pile dwindled enough we would start up again. Strange things were happening though - our lead was disappearing faster than we were selling it. Unbeknown to us, another couple of kids had also started up in the lead-nicking business. Going to our storeroom one day we caught them bang at it, as there they were coming out of our store carrying sacks, obviously, by the way they were struggling, full of our lead. We charged right at them, shouting at the top of our voices, 'Oi you, what's your game?'

Dropping their sacks they took to their heels, with us belting along after them shouting, 'Stop you thieving bastards!' But they were not going to stop for anyone. That is until just as they were about to turn a corner, they ran smack into a copper. He grabbed hold of them by the scruffs of their necks, while we did a rapid U-turn and went back the way we had come as fast as we could. Fortunately for us, this copper wasn't our usual beat copper, and as neither he nor these two thieves knew us we didn't worry too much. But we didn't go anywhere near our stash of lead for a few days. When we did, our stock of lead was gone completely. We fancied these two thieves had told the copper what was going on, and that the police had been round and nicked all our lead. We promised ourselves that if we ever came across those two again we would kick the shit out of them, as what with all the hard work we had put into this business it was a bloody liberty what they had done. Now we had to start all over again.

Fortunately for us though we had another way to earn money, which was from empty beer bottles and also lemonade ones. We learnt of this from our mum. One day, after one of the parties at our house she told us to take the empty bottles back to the pub, and to make sure that we got the returned bottle money on them. Usually my brother and I were nowhere in sight when there were errands to be run, leaving that sort of stuff to my sister. But if there was money to be earnt we didn't mind at all. After taking the first lot back and getting the money from the landlord, we were always on the lookout for beer bottles, even knocking on people's doors asking if they had any empties. One soppy old prat said yes one time, and passed us out a couple of carrier bags full, which pleased us no end until we found out they were all milk bottles, for which we got nothing. That was one house we never knocked on again. At the time though we didn't realise that we couldn't get money for milk bottles, so off we went to the local dairy, to get money for them. We handed them over to the bloke working there. He took them and said, 'Thank you boys,' and then got on with his work, while we just stood there waiting and staring at him. Eventually he looked up and said, 'Well boys, what can I do for you?' We told him we wanted our money.

'What money?' he asked.

'The money for the bottles,' we told him.

'But I don't give money for bottles,' was his reply to that. Now he was really pissing us off.

Dave said to him, 'Don't take liberties mate, the pub gives us money for empties and so should you.'

The shopkeeper started to get annoyed then and told us to get out of his shop, and started to come round the counter at us. We left a bit rapidly then, but on leaving shouted back at him, 'We will get you, you bastard!'

I personally thought, 'Sod this for a lark!' No sooner had we got our revenge on one person than another one popped up. Now we were back to two again, Chocolate Joe and this bloke in the dairy.

Our revenge on him though came very quickly. We knew that each day he had a couple of crates of milk delivered outside his shop early in the morning. The three of us arranged to meet the next morning, which we did, arriving outside his shop before he opened up. There were crates of milk which we nicked, taking them to a bombed house. Once there we drank a couple of bottles each, and then smashed them against the wall. Back we went to the shop. At last, down came the feller to open up. Finding no milk, back in he went, but time after time he popped out, even looking up and down the street, but still no milk. Eventually we got bored with him popping in and out, and off we went. Later that day my mother sent my sister round to the shop to get milk, but of course she got none, and nor did a lot of people in our street. The dairy man could get no more as he had had his quota for the day. I know he had a hump about his milk being nicked as people were saying how upset he was about it. Of course we kept very quiet about our part in this, as not only was the dairy bloke uptight about it, so were my mum and neighbours. There was no way we could let this dairy man know of our victory over him. What we did though was to go running by his shop shouting, 'Got any milk today mate?' From then on we kept to beer bottles.

One day, having taken quite a few bottles back to the pub, the publican told us to hang on for a minute before he paid us. Then taking the bottles we had given to him, he took them out of a doorway and into the backyard of the pub, where he put the empties we had given him in crates that were already in the yard. This gave us the idea of climbing over the back wall of the pub, which was easy to do, and nicking the empty bottles back again. We were very successful at this, and the publican bought bottles back off of us several times over. That is until one day, after feeling so pleased with ourselves, it all came unstuck. Taking some empties back that we had nicked from the backyard of the pub, the publican acted a bit stand-offish to us. Taking the bottles from us he began to look at each one. Having finished that he said, 'Right you three cow sons, I shall be seeing your mothers about you, get out of the pub and don't let me see any of you anywhere near here again.'

Looking at him in complete amazement I asked him, 'What's up with you Guv?'

Pointing at the bottles we had given him he replied, 'That's what's up with me,' and showed a stamp mark on each of the bottles. 'These fucking bottles are already mine and you little bastards have been nicking them from my backyard.'

It seemed that as he was getting more empties back than he was selling full ones, he had set up a system of marking the bottles as they were returned, to find out what was going on. We left the pub without arguing the toss with him as he was the type of bloke likely to give us a whack round the chops. But it meant another of our business ventures had bit the dust. It was good while it lasted, and the three of us were confident we would find something else to earn money from.

After the rest we had from nicking lead, we decided to go back to that, but even that was becoming hard work. No one wanted furniture, so looting was out. Getting lead was hard work not because there was a shortage, but because the wardens were becoming more watchful. They were continually chasing kids from the bomb sites, and it seemed that a lot of people who had moved out of London because of the bombing were now moving back again. Back came a lot of our old gang. Houses that were empty, even those only part inhabitable, were now becoming occupied so there was less chance of nicking things. Now all our businesses were failing. We really had to find something else, we had become so used to having a few bob in our pockets that we didn't like being skint one little bit.

Feeling this way brought on the revenge attack on Chocolate Joe's. Of course it was no good smashing his shop window again, that had already brought us a lot of sadness trying to eat his dummy sweets. This time we were going to smash the window in the shop door, and get into the shop itself. Once again we had to wait for the sirens to go off in the evening. This time our wait was not so long, as now we were not fussy on what night that happened, weekday or weekend made no difference to us. It turned out to be a weekday. Off went the sirens, the only problem was that not too many people were going to the shelters now. But our determination was such that we were not going to let a small thing like that bother us. As soon as the siren began to wail on the night in question, Dave, my brother and I grabbed our sacks and a brick, and off we flew to Chocolate Joe's. This time pretending to run by the shop, Dave let the brick go at the window and crash, in it went.

We continued to run for a few more yards, then stopping and looking back, and seeing that we had attracted no attention, straight into the shop we went. We were now well and truly amongst the goods. This time though we were not going to fall for any of Chocolate Joe's tricks. We had had enough of that crafty bastard!

As we went about filling our sacks, we were also tasting a sweet here and there. These sweets we were now putting in our sacks were the real thing, which gladdened our hearts. Having filled our sacks we left the shop. A bit of a job that was too, so full were our sacks, we really had to give them a tug or two to get them through the broken window, but there was no way that we were going to lessen our load to make things easier. Besides the sweets we had also got ourselves a bit of a bonus, as under the shop counter we had come across a biscuit tin full of money, all in coins: shillings, tanners and a few half crowns. There was no problem in getting the stuff home, we just walked boldly through the streets with the few passers-by taking no notice of us at all. This time though we did not take our loot into my house, but down to the basement of the house, as that was not occupied, being condemned as uninhabitable. Having arrived safely we lit an old oil lamp we had there, and began to sort out the sweets, putting a few aside to scoff later. Having done that the sacks of sweets were safely put under lock and key in a cupboard tucked away in the corner of the basement.

The next task was to count the money in the biscuit tin. Yes, we had left that to last, the sweets at the time having more importance to us. Having counted the money we had twenty pounds each. At last we were millionaires! The three of us sat there, chocolate-covered mouths smiling at each other. I think the sight of so much money must have frightened us a bit as taking just a shilling each, we took the tin full of money and hid it behind some loose bricks in a wall out in the backyard, with no intention of touching it except for a shilling here and there. Coming back in we made sure that the door to the backyard was securely locked. Why we did this I don't really know. Having locked the door from the inside, the sweets were fairly safe, but the money locked out in the yard was open to all sorts of thieves to get hold of. But Dave, my brother and myself were all quite happy with the arrangements. The night was now over and happily we went to our homes for an early night, for a change.

The next day the three of us even went to school but with our pockets full of sweets, sweets that we handed to everyone at the school. A couple of days of doing this and our stockpile had dwindled away to none. There were so many sweets in the school that kids were even offering them to teachers, the teachers politely refusing as they knew the hardships of the kids, what with rationing. But some of the kids insisted, 'Go on miss, we've got loads of sweets and can get more.' This cast a shadow of doubt in the teachers' minds as to where this sweet bonanza was coming from. It didn't take long to get to Dave, my brother and myself. We were questioned by the headmaster but he got nowhere with us. The day after the headmaster had questioned us, the local copper was brought to the school, the whole school being assembled in the main hall.

First the headmaster addressed us saying, 'It has been brought to my attention that there has been an abundance of sweets being handed around the school. A matter of deep suspicion to me. Which is why this police officer is here to talk to you.' He then handed over to the copper.

Up stood the copper and began, 'Boys and girls, a very serious crime has been committed.'

'OOOH!' we all went.

The copper continued, 'Chocolate Joe's in Church Street was broken into and a great many sweets have been stolen.'

'AAAH!' everyone went, turning their heads in our direction, looking at us accusingly. But we had turned our heads in the same direction as them. There was one problem with this; when they all turned their heads they were looking at us, while in turning ours we were staring at a brick wall about a foot from our noses.

The copper went on saying, 'Now we have a good idea who the culprits are for this nasty crime. We also believe all the stolen sweets are in this school, some of them even being here now. What we intend to do is to have you all file past this table and put any sweets you have on it. None of you will get into any trouble. We are only after the culprits.'

So the march past began, but strangely no sweets appeared on the table. As kids filed past they could be heard to say to the copper, 'We ain't got no sweets mister, we ain't got nuffink.'

When it came to our turn, we each said pretty much the same,

'We ain't done nuffink.'

We, like all the others, put no sweets on the table, but as I passed the table the headmaster said, 'Ronald stand there,' pointing to the end of the table. He did exactly the same with Dave and my brother. So there we stood while the rest of the school filed past and left the hall, leaving behind the three of us, the copper and the headmaster. Scattered around the hall floor where all the kids had been sitting were small piles of sweets.

The three of us were taken to the headmaster's office where we were questioned further. It appeared a lot of the other kids had been questioned before us, and each one had told the headmaster and the copper that Dave, my brother John and I had been giving everyone sweets in the past few days. In fact since Chocolate Joe's had been broken into. Our mothers were called to school and told the facts. We tried to keep up the pretence that we hadn't done anything, even going as far as to say we had found the sweets in the street, but that did us no good and we were taken to the police station. We were questioned further and in the end admitted breaking into the shop. Only at the police station were we asked about the money, each of us insisting we knew nothing about it, and that we had only nicked sweets. We were also questioned about breaking the window the first time and nicking the dummy sweets, but we denied that too. Eventually we were charged only with breaking in and nicking the sweets on the second occasion, and heard no more about the money or the dummies. We were then allowed to go home, but our mums had been given a date when they had to take us to court. On getting home my brother and I were made to go straight to bed. Dave, we found out later, got the same treatment as us. One good thing came out of it though - the headmaster told our mothers to keep us away from school until the court case was over.

going to America

AFTER PUTTING UP WITH OUR MOANING for a couple of days, our mother let us out of the house telling us, 'Go on, get out of my fucking sight, and stay out of trouble or I will give you a bloody good hiding.' I think she knew it was only a matter of time, and that we were just waiting for the weekend to come, and that when she went to the pub on Friday and Saturday nights, we would go out too, that we would risk getting beat up by her if she caught us. We had got used to her beating us anyway, and learnt to cover up and dodge the more vicious blows. Her giving us a good hiding even became a bit of a game; ducking away from blows and running round the kitchen table with our mother chasing us, screaming for us to stand still so she could whack us. After we got clear or she got fed up whacking us, I used to laugh at the thought of her expecting us to stand still while she gave us a kick up the arse or whatever. Anyway, we were free again.

Now though we were in a bit of a panic. We knew that we had to go back in front of the three old women we had been up in front of before, and they had said they would send us away next time we got into trouble. We didn't fancy getting evacuated again (which we imagined she was on about with this threat) so we decided to piss off out of it, and go to America, thinking we had enough money in the biscuit tin in the backyard to be able to do that. Once having made the decision, we made plans. First of all we had to get to a seaside town where there were boats. The only town we knew like that was Southend where we had been taken once. That set in our minds, we now had to wait until Friday night when our mum went to the pub, which would give the three of us a few hours start before we were found missing. Friday night came, and bang on time out went my mother. My brother and I stuffed some cleanish clothes into an old carrier bag, then went to the backyard to get the tin of money. Counting the money into three piles, we both took our share, and one of us took Dave's to give him when we met as arranged. Twenty pounds each all in coins was very weighty, but as we were so rich now that did not concern us in the least. My sister wanted to come to America with us, but we spun her an old story about how dangerous it could be and that our ship could be sunk by Germans. So she decided to stay in bed but promised not to tell our mother where we were going. Meeting Dave as planned we gave him his twenty pounds. The three of us then set off for the station to catch the train to Southend.

Arriving at the station each of us bought a platform ticket as there was no way we were going to spend our own money on train fares. There was a fairly long wait for the train which suited us as quite a few fellow travellers gathered on the platform, who we mixed with pretending to be with one or other of them. Eventually we were on our way. The journey itself was uneventful, so much so that we didn't even attempt to hide, arriving at Southend feeling very pleased with ourselves. But we were in for a bit of a shock as there standing at the ticket barrier was a copper talking to the ticket collector. There also seemed to be quite a few soldiers about with MP arm bands on. Surely they were not all out looking for us. We hid behind a couple of pillars, all the while keeping a careful eye on the activity at the barrier. It soon became clear that the only people being stopped was those in uniform. Even though that was a relief, we still could not pass through the ticket barrier with just a platform ticket, so our wait went on. When all became quiet we sidled up to the now locked barrier, but a barrier now clear of ticket collectors and MPs. Then all together we leaped the barrier and ran as fast as we could out of the station, all the while expecting shouts of 'STOP!' to follow us, but no such shouts came. We were away and over our first hurdle. Now we had to make our way down to the sea and then find a ship. Only having been to Southend once we did not remember where the sea was, so with our carrier bags of clothes and weighted down with pockets full of coins, we wandered around a few streets.

Time was getting on and we were becoming tired. Coming across a lady walking along towards us, we decided to take the bull by the horns and ask her the way. This was something we didn't really want to do, we did not want to talk to anyone just in case the police were looking for us, the army come to that. But ask we did. Dave stopped the lady and said, 'Excuse me missus, which way's the sea?'

Straight away we knew it was a mistake as the nosey cow asked, 'What are you kids doing out at this time of night, and why do you want to know where the sea is? Where do you live and what have you got in those carriers? Are you runaways?'

It's a wonder the bloody woman didn't suffocate as she came out with that little lot all in one go without drawing breath once. We had to get away from this nosey prat a bit quick. We took to our heels and legged it as fast as we could away from her. This time, unlike the ticket barrier, there were shouts after us. She was shouting, 'Come back. I'm going to call the police!' Some people really are mad I thought. As if anyone was going to come back if someone was going to call the police to them. But now she had our description, the first thing to do was to dump our carrier bags. Although our clothes were in them, we had enough money to buy some new ones when we reached America, so we were not fussed.

After walking around for a few more minutes we found the sea, but where were all the ships? There wasn't one in sight. The seafront was in complete darkness. The blaze of lights from the seafront stores and amusement arcades was not there. This was not the Southend we knew. Not that we were surprised at the darkness, what with blackouts being in force. In fact the blackout was part of our plan for stowing away on a ship. It would have helped us if there had been a ship in sight. On the beach where there used to be boats there was now just beach. Up and down the beach we walked, becoming more and more despondent. What could we do now? Tiredness settled in, and giving up hope of finding a boat we decided to find somewhere to sleep. Perhaps things would be different in the morning, maybe all the ships were at sea. So still hopeful we looked for somewhere to get our heads down, but where? We could hardly book into a hotel, as like the woman we had asked where the sea was, people in hotels may have become suspicious. It seemed to me that people the world over didn't trust kids. They always seemed to be asking questions like, 'Why aren't you at school?' or, 'What you kids been up to?' Even if we were standing on a street corner doing nothing, not even making a noise, some adult would come along and say, 'Why don't you kids find something to do?' Then when we did we would get, 'Why don't you kids stop doing that?' It was enough to drive a kid potty. But at Southend booking into a hotel was definitely out. We thought of going back to the shop doorway where we had dumped our clothes and sleeping there, but none of us could remember where it was. We wandered around for what seemed like hours. Then suddenly we found our place to stay. It was right up our street too, a boarded-up house just like those that we used to make our dens in all those years ago.

There stood this house in total darkness with its boarded-up windows. There didn't seem to be much bomb damage to it, in fact none at all. That, if anything, made it all the better as none of us really fancied sleeping in a bombed house. One other thing that made this house good for us, it was smack on the seafront so we could keep watch from there for any ships that came in. Getting one of the boards from one of the windows in the house was really easy, much easier in fact than the ones we took down at home. These boards opened just like doors, and had hinges fixed to them and the walls. Having opened these boards at one window, we found that the window was locked. That caused little problem, it was just a matter of finding a stone on the beach and crash, in went the window. Not even waiting to see if we had disturbed anyone, we opened the window and that was us inside. What a shock we were in for.

Striking matches to have a look round, we discovered the place was fully furnished. But what sort of place was this we were in? The king must live here. The furniture seemed to be painted a gold colour. There were paintings hanging on all the walls. Over the fireplace was a huge mirror, china and ornaments was everywhere. There was a great big clock standing on the floor and nearly reaching the ceiling. On a table in the centre of the room stood an oil lamp. Closing these 'door things' on the windows, we lit the lamp. Sitting down in these great big armchairs we all lit up fags and talked over what we were going to do. The aim was the same: get to America. We even spoke about all this lovely furniture, and commented on how good it would have been if this house had been in London so that we could have looted it. Mind you, I don't think my mum would have liked this furniture as it was a bit posh. Feeling hungry we decided to look the rest of the house over. On going to the door though, we found it to be locked. We were stuck in this room. The only way in and out was through the window we had come through. That left us with nothing to do but go to sleep, and wait until morning to feed our faces.

It seemed to me that I had only been asleep for a little while before someone was shaking me by the shoulder. Thinking it was one of the others I shouted, 'Piss off, go back to sleep!' My shoulder was now shook much harder. Opening my eyes I found myself staring up into the face of a copper. With him was another copper and an old couple in dressing gowns. Daylight was streaming through the now open window. I felt sure we had shut them the night before. It seemed this house was not an empty one at all. There was a family living there, two of whom were standing in front of us now in their dressing gowns. We were made to stand in a line, but for what seemed ages no one spoke to us, the four of them just standing and staring right at us. This made me a bit fidgety, but I wasn't going to speak to them; if they didn't want to talk, sod 'em! Eventually one of the coppers did speak saying, 'What do you think you're doing here?'

'Going to America,' said Dave.

'Going to America,' said my brother, and not to be outdone, 'Going to America,' I said.

We were questioned as to where we had come from, giving all the information freely. 'Why are you going to America?' we were asked. Between us we told of how we were fed up, that this woman at court, when we went there, had said she would put us away if we got into any more trouble. As we had got into more trouble, we were going to America, as we didn't want to be evacuated again. I think all these people found all this a bit confusing as they just stood in front of us looking stunned.

The outcome was that we were taken to the local police station. There we were left in a room to wait for our mothers to come to collect us. We should think ourselves lucky, we were told, as the people whose house we had broken into did not want to press charges. We had been searched, and of course all the money we had was taken off of us. They wanted to know where we got all the money from and, bloody cheek, they even asked us if we had broken into anywhere else. Anyway, they took all the money away from us. Eventually our mothers arrived. They were told about the money, the Southend police telling them it would be handed over to police in London, who had been contacted. It was believed the money was the missing money from Chocolate Joe's, and would probably be returned to him. This Chocolate Joe, in spite of the fact that none of us had ever met him, seemed to be nothing but trouble for us. We really would have to get him.

All the way home on the train we were told how we were going to be killed when we got there. Well, we were obviously not killed, but good attempts were made on our lives. My mother really went into one, 'I'll give you America, you little bastards,' whack, whack, whack round the head. 'I've had to pay out a lot of money coming to get you two,' another good whacking round the head. 'Why didn't you tell me about this fucking money?' This time it was kick, kick, kick. 'Get undressed, get into bed and bloody well stay there, you ain't ever going out again.' Whack, whack, whack. All this time we never said a word, there was no point in that, and in any case we were far too busy dodging the whack whack whacks raining down on us. Needless to say, when our mother had gone to work we were up and out, in spite of being under threat of strangulation if we did. We just had to make sure to be back in before she got home.

Our confinement did not last too long anyway. As our bedroom was also the kitchen-come-sitting room, and our bed took up half the room, we were a nuisance to my mother and her cronies, who could hardly sit about in the same room as us gossiping about who was having it with who, and talking about, 'That old whore down the road'. So it was, 'Get up and get out, but make sure you're back in by eight,' which we never were. But as long as my mother had her mates with her, drinking tea (or gin if they had any) it wasn't noticed or was ignored when we got in late. If my mother had been on the gin she was a bit of a pest as when we came in from the street she would get soppy and want to give us sloppy kisses. I didn't like that at all. I would have preferred a couple of whacks as then she would have been the mum I knew.

Eventually it came to the time that Dave, my brother and myself had to go back to court. The start of that day was horrible as we were made to have a bath and put on our best clothes. My best clothes had been my best for some time now. My best clothes now fitted only where they touched, so instead of looking my best I looked like a clown. But it was too late to do anything about that. Getting ready to go to court also meant a continuous stream of orders from my mother: 'You two had better behave yourselves,' 'Keep your socks pulled up,' and 'You had better not let me catch you wiping your noses on your sleeves. Make sure you use the bit of old rag I've given you.' The last word of warning we got was, 'If you show me up you're in deep trouble.' That was one thing with my mother, if we were ever out with her (which was seldom) we always had the same warning: 'You had better not show me up.' Just before we left the house she called both of us over to her, put her arms around us, gave us both a kiss and said, 'Be good boys.' She had a sad look about her.

Back at the court it looked exactly the same. The same three old girls sat behind the long table. We had to sit in the same three chairs, our mothers behind us. It was as if nothing had moved, as if we were a setting for a Madame Tussaud's waxworks. We were asked if we had broken into Chocolate Joe's, although that was not the name they said, but we knew what they meant. The copper got up and did his piece. He even told the three old girls that we had run away from home, but not about our trying to get to America. Our school attendance was read out which took about two seconds. Then the old girl in the middle leant forward to the other two either side of her, and began to whisper. As she leant forward, so did we to see if we could earwig, but no luck. The three old girls sat back up, so too did the three young boys.

The old girl in the middle was again the one to do all the talking, she must have been the chief. She began to give us a lecture, only this time it was more severe. It all amounted to us (according to her) being beyond parental control; that we wouldn't attend school, that we ran around causing havoc and it had to be stopped. We would all go to an approved school for three years. Well I thought, that isn't too bad. What an approved school was I hadn't a clue, but if this mob thought that they could make us go to school for three years they had another thing coming. We would just hop the wag. As we were being led out of the courtroom our mothers really began to cry. Why they were crying I couldn't think. Were they crying because we had to go to school for three years? Surely not. They had been trying to get us to go to school for years. Suddenly two men came up to us and said, 'Right you three, come with us.' Dave was taken away separately. I later found out that because he was a Catholic he had to go to a different place than my brother and me. The last words my mother spoke to us was, 'Be good boys, I will come to see you.'

Now this looked serious. What the hell was she on about? We would be going home with her soon. These two men took us out of the court building through a back door, and then along a path to another building. Arriving there one of them rang a doorbell. Neither my brother or myself seemed to have the heart to ask either of these two men where we were going. In our hearts I think we knew that we were not going home. The door was opened in answer to the man's ring by another man who we were handed over to. Once we were inside the building the door was locked behind us. There were other boys standing around, and others we could see in a playground through a window. Now this seemed ok, this must be the approved school we had to attend, and it was only fifteen minutes from where we lived. So what my mother was on about coming to see us for I didn't know as we would be home by teatime.

We were taken along a corridor and told to stand with our backs to the wall outside of the headmaster's office. The two of us were then called into the office together. Then we knew we were not going home, that this was no ordinary school. No wonder our mums were crying. I felt like crying myself. The headmaster said words to the effect: 'Right you two, you have been sent here by the court and here you will stay until we can find other schools to send you to. It is easy to escape from here, but you will be caught and fetched back, and you will be severely punished. If you break any rules of the school you will be punished. Now get out.' So out we got.

Waiting for us outside was another master. We were made to have a bath. This was getting to be a bit too much. We had already had one bath that day before going to court. Two in one day was going over the top when we were used to two a month. We were then taken, with towels wrapped around our waists, to see a nurse in a hospital room. But what was this? This was more like the school we knew as this nurse was another Nitty Nora. She, like all Nitty Noras, went through our heads with a fine-tooth comb. Of course she found nits, as usual we were lousy. This Nitty Nora only washed our heads though and didn't paint us with a brush like they did up The Bake. Once this was done we were issued with clean clothes which neither of us liked as they were all the same, and, as we were to find, every boy was dressed like us too. Then we were taken to a big room with rows of two-tier bunk beds in, given a bed each, and told to stay there until we were called for tea.

Once alone we talked. We both agreed that there was no way we were going to stay here, we just had to get out. We knew that it wasn't going to be easy, that it wasn't just a matter of hopping the wag as in an ordinary school. This was a matter of making an escape, something to be planned. Talking with our heads close together, no one else was to hear our plans. When the other kids began to come into the room, we came out of our huddle. Once all the other kids were in the room some came over to talk to us. There was one boy who we were going to stay well clear of. He appeared to be much older than the rest of us. From what we were told by some of the others he was the house captain and a right bloody sneak too. Evidently if any of us did anything wrong then he would report us to one of the masters.

It was an odd carry on here as there were two parts to this school. Some nutter in the past must have thought it was a ship, one side of the place being called port, the other starboard. I've no recollection of whether I was port or starboard. Come to think of it, nor did I while I was there. To me this was the dining room and this was where I slept, and that sort of thing was plenty good enough for me without all this old cobblers of port and starboard.

Anyway, came our first meal which was tea. We all had to stand behind our chairs at our allotted tables and grace would be said. Then the shout would go up from one of the masters, 'Port sit.' A minute later, 'Starboard sit.' Evidently this call was alternated each meal time so that each side got to sit first in strict order. This completely baffled me. I always had my arse half in the seat as soon as the first cry went up. This, or any other form of breaking the rules, would lead to a demerit. If you got a certain number of demerits, you were made to go to bed as soon as tea was over. In the evenings after school - and everyone had to go to classes - we were allowed to play games of one sort or another until seven thirty. Then it was time for a wash and then bed by eight. Lights would be put out by eight thirty, anyone caught talking after lights out would find themselves bang in trouble. For that offence the culprit would be made to stand at the foot of his bed for hours on end. All this we were told on our first day by other boys. When lights were switched out, there was one that was left on throughout the night, a red light stuck in the middle of the ceiling which cast a warm glow around the room. We were warned about one master, who it appeared that as soon as he turned the main light off would then go round each bed and pat each boy on the arse and rest his hand there for a while. I was told he was a dirty old bastard. What all the fuss was about I at first couldn't make out, but soon had it explained to me.

Now I knew why he was a dirty old bastard. A couple of nights after we got there the warning went round that he was on. When everyone was in bed and he started his rounds, I lay on my back watching a couple of the unwary (if that is what they were) have their arses patted. Most of the boys lay on their sides facing him. Still he patted them, even if it was just on the leg. I could sense him near me. Then none too gently, pat, pat, pat. With a shout I sat bolt upright, while he jumped back a couple of paces. The dirty old git had patted me right on the bollocks. Because I shouted in pain, I got a demerit. It was a good job we didn't intend to stay there too long as I didn't fancy getting hit in the cobblers every night!

After three or four days in this place my brother and I had had enough, but we had also found a way out. There was no way out of the buildings themselves, the windows were all screwed up, the doors always locked. Finally there was always a master around, and, worse of all, the bigger boy house captain was always mooching about and poking his nose into things. Luckily he never interfered with us. Perhaps he knew we were brothers, and that we would both jump him if he bothered either one of us. That's how it would have been with the flash sod if he had.

The way we had found to get out was a bit risky but it was the only way we could see. Unfortunately our escape also had to be in broad daylight and very quick. Each day we were allowed on to the yard to kick a football around, or just run around in general. The yard was thought to be safe, as first it was sur-rounded by a six-foot-high wooden fence. On top of that was chicken wire rising another four foot. At one point, though, the fence joined one end of the building. At the corner, where fence joined building, was a window with a sill about five feet off of the ground. That was our target: on to the sill, a jump, grab the top of the wire and away. One other good point about this was that the window we were going to use was not overlooked by any other window. As we were let out into the yard on our own this was ideal. The only problem we could see was if one of the other boys saw what we were up to and shouted out. Especially the prat of a house captain.

The first time we were let out into the yard was to be the time. When that time came, we followed the rest of the school outside, and with them began to kick a ball around. Getting the ball and running with it to the end of the yard where we wanted to be was no problem. Once there we turned, and with an almighty kick belted the ball high in the air, back to the end of the yard furthest away from us. As all the other boys rushed after it my brother and myself took off to our window sill, he going first while I kept a watchful eye on the yard. As quick as a flash he was on the sill, and with a leap jumped and caught the top of the wire while I began to get myself on to the sill ready to follow him. Then disaster struck. As my brother grabbed at the top of the wire it came crashing to the ground with some of the fence, and my brother with it. He landed flat on his back covered in chicken wire and fencing. I must admit that under any other circumstances I would have laughed my head off at the sight, but there wasn't time for that as the crash had drawn attention to us, and now there was shouting from one or two other boys. Hastily I pulled the wire and other debris from my brother who regained his feet and breath. By now there was a horde of boys running in our direction, whether to join us or stop us I know not, the two of us not wanting to find out. We both took a running jump at what was left of the fence and went through it like a bull in china shop. But what was this? We were now in someone's back garden surrounded by a six foot wall on three sides; the fourth side, which should have been the fence, we had now demolished.

Standing in this garden, with a rake held aloft in his hands, was the master who liked to pat little boys' bums, and who had nearly demerited my balls. Now here he was giving me another smack up the cobblers by catching us. We were frogmarched back into the building and into our dormitory where we were made to pack all of our kit. Frogmarched out again, down a corridor, and both locked into single rooms where we were told we would stay until we were moved to a different school, which happened within a couple of days. Only this time it was all a bit shattering as we were split up. At the time I did not know where my mate Dave had gone, except that it was to a Catholic school, and now I did not know where my brother was going to. Me, well I was heading for Sussex, to Mile Oak approved school, very near Brighton.

six of the best

HERE I WAS, NOT YET TWELVE, entering a strange land. I was taken there by car, driven by one of the masters from Stamford House, which was the name of the place I had been held in so far. We seemed to drive for hours. Not a word was spoken between us, which I was pleased about, as there was no way I wanted to talk to this bastard driving me further and further from my home. Yes, I blamed him and all the other people that I had come in contact with from the start for all this.

Our journey's end was now in sight. Driving into a narrow lane at the entrance of which was a house on either side, we drove along this winding road with fields surrounding it. Suddenly the lane petered out and there before us was this huge house covered in ivy. There was a half-circular drive in front of it and the whole place was covered with flowers, trees and bushes. What this place was I couldn't even dream, but it couldn't be the school that I was going to. It was far too posh for the likes of me. Rich kids went to places like this. Leaving the car we entered this large house, and yes I had arrived. This was my new school.

Once inside we were greeted by the largest man in the world, or so he seemed to me, he was so huge and very fat. These two masters did not seem to have a lot to say to each other. I was signed for and off went the bloke who had brought me here. I didn't particularly like him, but, standing in front of this giant, when he left it was as though I had lost a friend. Perhaps it was just that now I was alone, away from all my friends and family and the back streets of London. I was a bundle of nerves. For such a big man he had the squeakiest voice I had ever heard. It reminded me of Olive Oil out of Popeye. He was going on nine to the dozen about rules and regulations, and that if I ran away from here I would get six of the best when I was brought back. If I got caught out of bounds I would get six of the best, if I got caught smoking I would get six of the best, and, finally, if I didn't stop smirking, and get that silly grin off of my face, I would get six of the best. I was never more happy when along came another master and took me away from Olive Oil. What six of the best was I never had a clue never having been threatened with it before, but whatever it was it didn't sound too clever to me. Later I was to be given six of the best, and on some occasions twelve of the best. What was 'the best' about it I still can't imagine. Whoever thought up that phrase had to be a complete nutcase!

The first impression I got of the place was how sparkling clean it was. The cleaning lady must have worked really hard to keep everything so gleamingly clean and shiny. The school was built in a square shape, the front being offices and the headmaster's living quarters. The two opposite sides upstairs were dormitories, two on either side. Below them were the bath and shower rooms and dining hall. The fourth side was taken up by a gymnasium and a small swimming pool. All of these enclosed a playground. From all these buildings there were entrances that led to the outside, none of which were ever locked. This was the 'out of bounds' I'd heard about, and could lead to six of the best. Leaving through one of these entrances, unless with a master, was strictly taboo. We were confined to the buildings and the playground. From the dormitory windows could be seen nothing but countryside, and most of that being hills as we were smack in the middle of the Sussex Downs.

My first day there was to be taken up with being given two lots of clothing (one for summer, the other for the winter months), being allocated to a dormitory and generally shown round the place, being handed over to different masters as I went along. For all the good these introductions did me, one master to show me round would have been sufficient because each master told me the same thing - if I did this or that I would get six of the best. They all seemed obsessed with those words. Not one of them told me what I could do. It was enough to make a person terrified to even breathe. I still had the impression that I had ended up in a really posh gaff, and, what's more important, one I could easily get out of when I wanted to. Which was as soon as possible. I wasn't going to worry about all these threats that were being thrown at me because it hadn't bothered me when my mum used to beat me up. What this lot could do to me that she hadn't I couldn't imagine. So I cocked a deaf 'un to all their chat!

The last person I was to be seen by on my first day was the school matron. I at first thought she was to be another Nitty Nora, but far from it. She spoke to me quite kindly and explained to me that she was there to help. If I had trouble writing she would help me to write a letter home and so on. It was the matron who issued me with all the clothes I was given. All pretty uniform stuff so that we all looked the same. For none of us was there such a thing as trousers, which in a way gave us a laugh, as a few of the boys were taller than the masters and it looked weird to see a very tall boy in shorts talking to a short master in long trousers. This was another odd place though as the four dormitories in the place were not dormitories according to this mob, they were houses. Each house had a name: Allenby, Beattie, Haig and Jellico. Why the fuck they couldn't call them One, Two, Three and Four, like the classes back at school where I came from, was beyond me. How fancy could you get!

Came my first meal time, tea. Even in there it was all done by houses. One row of six tables being for Allenby with nine to a table, four sitting on either side and, what I was to find out, the head table boy sitting at the head of the table. This was at least on four of the tables, the head boys on the other two tables being the house captain and vice-captain. Usually it was the best fighters who had these head jobs. Nothing whatsoever to do with how old you were, and so on. If you could beat up any of these people eventually you would get their job. Not that in the time that I was there did I particularly want one of those jobs as you also had to be a sneak for the masters.

I had already been into my house to stow my kit away, which had to be just so. The dormitory, like the dining room, was set in rows of beds. Two rows down the centre, head to toe, the other two rows jutting out from the side walls. At one end of the dorm was a row of open-fronted lockers in which our spare clothes had to be neatly folded. If they weren't, six of the best. Beds had to be made tidily, so much so that standing by the doorway of the dorm every bed looked the same, and in exact lines, with pyjamas folded neatly at the foot. Now that was a thing, pyjamas, I'd never worn the bloody things. I had always slept in the nod, but now it seemed as if I had to wear them. Not doing so was to get me into trouble.

By now I had of course met and spoken to quite a few of the other boys, one of them in particular who I knew from my area back home. He was to become one of the best all-round sportsmen at the school, at boxing and cricket. It was he that wised me up to a lot of what went on at the place and who to avoid. We couldn't talk for too long as the day had flown by and it was now time for bed, and Dinky (this boy's name) not only lived in a different house to me but also on the other side of the yard. The first thing I learnt during my talk with Dinky, and some of the others, on my first evening there was that there was no cleaning lady, as I had thought, keeping this place so spotless. All the cleaning was done by the boys. This was done straight after breakfast, before school, each boy being given a task to perform, and perform it to the best he had better!

There was a points system at this place, for good behaviour, work done well and so on. Points could be won or lost for anything under the sun. Everyone would start the week with no points, and then as the week progressed get plus or minus points according to their behaviour. This points system, besides applying to the individual, also applied to each table in the dining room, and each house. During my time at the school this system led to more bullying by other boys than any system I've seen since. Any boy getting into trouble, and getting minus points for either his house or table, got a bloody good hiding from the others; they were beaten black and blue. These points were totted up at the end of each week. Once that was done various prizes were given out. The best table would get a special meal. The best house would get extra time with the lights on at night, lights that were usually turned out at eight o'clock. The best individual would get an extra sweet ration. The worst-behaved boy would have to stand to attention in the middle of the playground during every play time. The worst-behaved dormitory would have the lights put out as soon as they went to bed, which meant no talking or reading of comics. Talking after lights out was strictly forbidden, and was punishable by six of the best. As there were no masters on, except as night watchmen, it was left to house captains and their like to report any boy talking after lights out.

This points system amazed me for a variety of reasons. Take the boy who had been the worse behaved in any given week. There he would be, stuck in the middle of the playground until bed time, with no chance of getting into trouble by being out of bounds or whatever, yet he could be made culprit of the week for a second or even a third time. How the hell he did it I don't know. The same applied to the totting up of points at the end of the week. There was never a draw, only outright winners, that was something I did not believe could happen week after week. As I've said, the house captain and vice-captain were usually the best fighters, and so held their position of power until along came a boy who beat one or both of them up. It didn't matter how long you had been in the school either. This was my first day there, but if I had got into an argument with either the captain or vice-captain of the house, and beat them up, then within days I would have been given one of those positions. It was survival of the fittest with the compliance of the masters, their attitude being it was no good having a boy (or boys) in charge of other boys if one of the boys they were in charge of could beat them up. Why all the other boys just didn't gang together and beat the shit out of these bullies I don't know; it just seemed to be an acceptable thing to happen.

So to my first night in the dorm. I got into bed to read a comic that someone had lent me, when over came this house captain to tell me all the house rules as he saw them. Then he went on about how Allenby was the best house in the place, and that was how it was going to stay. Anyone who fucked it up would have him to deal with, and a lot of old cobblers like that. As he was spouting on I just sat there looking at him. This place took some looking into before any real plans were made. After this lecture he then told me that as I was the new boy I had to do the running about, but only for the night, and that tomorrow it would be back to normal; of a turn each. Well I thought I might as well go along with this to see how things worked out. We had to get on with things before the master came round for his final check and turned the lights out.

While he was telling me all this, other boys were wandering about all over the place. Some cleaning their shoes, others going out the dormitory door and into another room just outside. Anyway this house captain then asked me what I wanted for supper. I had a choice of kippers or custard. This seemed a bit of a dodgy choice to me. At the time I didn't like kippers so opted for the custard. I'd never heard of anyone having custard for supper before, but who knew what they got up to in Sussex. So following him I went out of the dormitory door and into the room I had seen quite a few of the other boys going. Once in this room all hell broke loose. I was jumped on by all the others already there, no matter how much I struggled I was soon wrestled to the ground. About four boys then pissed all over me. I'd been initiated. Evidently if I had asked for kippers I would have been sent on a fool's errand to the lockers at the end of the dorm, and every boy in the dorm would have pelted me with their shoes. Ever since then I have always preferred kippers to custard.

The following day I had to go to school, feeling throughly pissed off for falling for the trick the night before, and determined to do some initiating myself before too long. Sitting in the classroom on my first day at school my mind wandered off. The teacher was spouting some old bollocks about King Harold or something in that line, but my thoughts were back in London, back to our old headquarters, to the gangs of kids that we used to do battle with. I felt a presence behind me before I had time to look up. Wallop! A ruler came crashing down onto the back of my hands. Leaping up from my desk, with a shout of, 'Ow, fuck that!' I was grabbed by the scruff of my neck, out of the classroom and over to the headmaster's office. He was told of what I had not being doing in class and then about my language. Olive Oil stood towering above me, but now his voice didn't sound so funny as he said, 'Right, six of the best for you. We do not allow idleness while in class and we certainly do not allow swearing.' I was then sent up to my dormitory until tea time, and there I had to stay with no lunch.

As I had a long wait for my punishment at tea time, I decided to have a bit of a kip. Stripping off and not bothering about pyjamas I hopped into bed and nodded off. But I was rudely awoken. A bomb had landed on the school or there was an earthquake as I woke with the bed on top of me. A voice was shouting, 'Come on, quick, out of there!' Panic-stricken, I quickly untangled myself from the bed clothes and got to my feet. There before me stood the reddest-faced school master that anyone could wish to see. Then a tornado did hit me. He started to slap out at me in a fury, all over my naked body. I was used to this; as I did with my mother, I avoided a lot of the blows. This was different though, I had never been slapped about when I had no clothes on, and the slaps that got through hurt, especially as he didn't seem to care where they landed: body, face, they all counted to him. With the hidings my mother had given to me not once had she ever struck me on the face, while this character did several times, and not pulling back on any of them. Although at the time I did not know the meaning of the word, I felt completely humiliated. I hated that man then as I hate him still to this day.

70

So far in my life I had not hated anyone, I took what was coming to me and that was that. This though was different.

It seems that I had slept through the afternoon, and it was now tea time, and time for my punishment. I was told to dress, and all the time I was doing so I was being berated by this bastard of a man: 'I can see you're going to learn the hard way, and I'm just the man to teach you.' Then with a final whack around the head I was told to follow him. As far as I was concerned if he was heading north I wanted to be heading south, but I had no option other than to follow him to the dining hall.

All the rest of the school were seated at their tables, backs straight. In front of them stood the headmaster, in his hand he had a cane which he was swishing through the air. Seeing me he shouted, 'You, stop there!' and then to the rest of the school he shouted, 'School, turn and face the back wall.'

Once this had been done to his satisfaction, he marched me none too gently out of the dining room to the long corridor outside. I was then told to bend over and touch my toes. When I had done this he came up behind me and grabbed the top of my shorts so that they were tight into the crack of my arse.

He then began to tell me, 'You are going to get six of the best, for swearing and idleness in class.' He was telling me this at the top of his squeaky voice so the rest of the school could hear. He finished off by telling me that if I stood up before the punishment was finished, for every time I did so another stroke of the cane would be given. He then walked away from me, but through my legs, as I was still bent over, I could see him marching away to the far end of the corridor. Once there he turned, and still watching him through my legs I could see him begin to run in my direction. I was determined not to stand up, but as soon as he got to me he gave a little jump in the air and down crashed the cane wrapping itself round my arse and the side of my hip. The pain of that I cannot describe. I had not felt such pain before or indeed since. I leapt up grabbing my arse; fortunately I did not cry out, if I had I'm sure it would have been to swear. I was grabbed by the neck and forced to bend over again. I still had six of the best to come, having earnt the extra one. Through those I did not rise or call out, and neither did I through the many canings I got after this first time.

I was never again going to show him the pain of being caned.

In fact there were a few boys in the school that when caned they would bend over without being told to, grip their ankles and, except through the force of the blows, not move an inch. Once the caning was over and done with they would just stand up, look the headmaster right in the face for a few seconds, and walk away with a bit of a strut. I believe this upset him more than anything else could.

Once my caning was over, the school could then sit down to their tea. That was the general routine for caning, and always at tea time. It didn't surprise me how many boys were put off their tea after a caning session. I myself was when I listened to this form of punishment being carried out most days of the week. After my first dose of six of the best I wasn't allowed to have tea. I was told that I must go to my dormitory and straight to bed, which was amazing really. I'd been slapped about for going to bed and now I'd been caned I had to go to bed! But my night wasn't over yet.

All the other boys came to the dorm at seven, this was the routine, summer and winter. The masters would be away to have their dinner, then at eight lights out. Anyway, when the others arrived in the dorm, they all wanted to look at my arse to see what it looked like after the caning. Now I can't see what the fascination was, but then it was the done thing; every boy that was caned showed his arse as the rest of the dorm filed past. One stupid boy having a look at my arse this first time asked, 'Did it hurt?' Well there was only one answer to that, 'Of course it fucking hurt!' I felt like punching this prat in the mouth for asking such a question. Now the only one who hadn't seen my arse was me, but not being a contortionist I couldn't get a proper look. Then the idea struck me to go to the toilet and have a look in the mirror above the sink, only to find that I couldn't see much, the mirror being too high. So the only thing to do was to climb onto the sink, that way I would get a long look. Standing on the sink and looking back, there it was, my multi-coloured arse. Suddenly I felt something move beneath my feet, and before I could do anything to avoid it, the sink went crashing to the floor, with me in it. There was such a crash the whole school must have heard it, and would be sure to fetch a master. So without hanging about I was out of that toilet and into bed before anyone arrived, and arrive they did. Of course everyone was having an early night, we were all under the blankets asleep. Nothing was said about the broken sink that night. The following night, the dormitory I was in, and the one that shared the same landing and toilet, had to be in bed by seven with lights out straight away, which didn't do my popularity any good.

This lights out at seven was for any misbehaviour in the dormitory. Anyone caught talking after lights out would mean lights would be put out early the following night. Various offences could mean early lights out. Some of these offences we knew about and could be avoided, others couldn't as it seemed they were made up as time passed. The dorm I was in didn't really get into too much trouble, the house captain saw to that, either by bullying or reporting people to the masters. A lot of the boys were fed up with him as at nights everyone wanted to get up to some sort of mischief. This captain had to be put in his place at some time or another, and there would come a time when he would be.

In each dorm there were a number of piss-the-beds; their beds were nearest to the doorway. To try to cure them of this habit the night watchman would come round a couple of times a night and shaking their shoulders would call out, 'Karzi! Karzi!' The piss-the-beds would then totter off to the toilet. In some cases this helped, in others boys still pissed the bed. Anyway, within ten minutes or so of the nightwatchman's first round, those of us still awake would get up and go round the piss-the-beds again, and just as the nightwatchman had done, shake the boys awake giving the call, 'Karzi! Karzi!' We did this several times during the night so between us and the nightwatchman the piss-the-beds would eventually be crawling out to the karzi. In the dorm that I was in there were about four piss-the-beds. Now the only people who liked the piss-the-beds were other piss-the-beds, so they got more stick than most. I had thought to myself that it was a pity this bunch didn't live round my area in London. The piss-the-bed gang! It was a good bet that they would have always been the Germans.

After having been in this place for a couple of months, I thought enough was enough - now it was time for me to go home. By this time I'd had six of the best for various reasons: smoking, being out of bounds and so on. I had become pals with another boy called Mick Cowans. He was going to run off with me. Where he was going to run to I had no idea, as he had no parents, and from what I could gather no other relations either. He had been sent to this approved school from an orphanage, not for thieving as most of us were here for. It seemed that he had kept running away from this orphanage. He just could not come to terms with the fact that he had no one to belong to. Now he was at Mile Oak he was even worse off than at the orphanage. At least there he was with other kids like himself that had no parents. Now he was in a place where everyone else had parents to come to visit them, and have them home for summer and Christmas leave. This in itself should have helped him to come to terms with the fact that he had no parents, but with Mick it had the reverse effect. He had the belief now that if everyone else at Mile Oak had parents, then somewhere so had he. He had several canings for running away from Mile Oak, just as he had at the orphanage. He had got used to it so much that this punishment had no effect on him whatsoever. Each time he had been brought back to Mile Oak after running away, he told those in charge that he had run away to find his mum and dad. Each time he was told, 'You have no mum and dad,' and was given six of the best. As he was my best mate at this approved school I tried to tell him that he had no parents, but he got upset and I had to say sorry.

Mick had travelled miles in his search for his mum and dad and now he was going to run away to London with me to see if he could find them there. He even asked me if I could help him when we got to London. I could do no more than say yes I would. To run away and get caught, and then be brought back to the school was to earn the runaway twelve of the best. Mick had many twelve stroke canings, as yet I had none, but that was to come. All I could hope for Mick was that wherever his dead parents were they knew about him, as no one I have ever met loved his parents more than he did, and he didn't even know what they looked like.

So Mick and I made our plans. We intended to leave the dorm at about nine o'clock at night, which would give the night watchman time to do his first Karzi Karzi bit and settle down for a while before his next tour. Came the night we were going to do our runner. We did as normal: undressed, went to bed and so on, and there we waited for the watchman to do his first call. Once that was over with we were out of bed and dressed as quick as a flash. Looking around the dorm most of the boys appeared to be asleep.

Attached to each dorm was a fire escape, a metal stairway running down the outside of the building. This was to be our route out. We didn't want to go down the internal stairs for fear of bumping into one of the masters, some of who lived in the same part of the building we did. Making our way to the fire exit door, a voice called out, 'Where do you two think you're going?' Looking back, there was the house captain sitting up in bed staring at us. We were not going to stand for any of his old bollocks now, we were ready to go and that was that, Mick even more so than me. He called back, 'Mind your own business and keep your fucking mouth shut!' A look of surprise came over the captain's face, I don't think he had been spoken to in that way for a long time. He just sat there staring as Mick and I disappeared down the fire stairs.

It was our intention to make our way to Portslade station and then jump a train to anywhere, to at least get us as far away from Mile Oak as soon as possible. One thing I wasn't going to do was to catch another Marlowe Donkey. We got to Portslade with no problems at all. At the station it was a simple thing to get on to the platform, as it was a level crossing station. It was just a matter of getting under the crossing gate and there was the platform.

A short wait and in came a train. We found ourselves an empty carriage and settled down, making no attempt to hide. If a ticket collector came round we would tell him that our parents were in the toilet, and if he got too stroppy we would pull the communication cord and jump off the train. So alert were we we didn't even notice that it was a non-corridor train, which worked in our favour, or should have done. So we settled into this nice warm and comfortable carriage.

It could not have been too long after that we were being woken up by a porter and a copper. We were at Brighton station. From that station we were taken to the police station, there to wait for someone to collect us from Mile Oak. We were not even asked who we were or where we had come from. It seemed these people only had to look at us and they knew we were approved school boys. It didn't take too long for us to be called for and to get back to Mile Oak.

Now I was, for the first time, going to get twelve of the best, with Mick the umpteenth. This time there was going to be a change in the routine. The headmaster really had the hump with us two for disturbing his night that he got to work with his cane as soon as we arrived back. It's boring to go on repeating myself over this caning lark so I shall press on. Back in the dorm we woke everyone up with the noise of our entry. The first one awake just had to be the house captain, sneering at us that he knew we would be caught, and how did our arses feel with twelve of the best. Now I had had enough of him as well as the school. Walking casually up to his bed I pounced, smashing him straight in the mouth. Once I had done that there was uproar with boys calling out for me to beat the bastard up. I had taken this boy by complete surprise, and before he could react Mick also jumped in and began to beat him. Suddenly there was a shout from the dorm door, 'Nitto master.' Everyone got into bed as quickly as possible. When the master arrived everything was quiet, and he did not take it upon himself to ask what all the noise was. We were all saved by the boy who had run to the door as soon as the trouble had started. This was normal practice. When anything took place in the dorm that shouldn't have been going on, one boy or another ran to the door to keep watch.

The next day it was noticeable that the house captain had a thick lip and a bit of a black eye. He was asked by one or two of the masters what had happened, but good for him he kept his mouth shut. Although he stayed as house captain, no one else wanting the job, we became if not friends at least not enemies. He even joined in on some of the night-time fuck-abouts. He had been fetched down a peg or two. I think he also got the message that if he started on either Mick or me then he would have the two of us on him. One at a time he could probably beat us up, but never together.

nicking sweets no matter what

I HADN'T BEEN AT THIS PLACE FOR TOO LONG, and with my arse seemingly going to be one massive bruise forever, I began to wonder if I should try to settle down and behave myself. All reason told me that I should, but I didn't. In spite of the cane it was much more fun to be into something that could lead me to trouble than it was to ponce about being a good boy. I had found in Mile Oak that it didn't work anyway to keep out of bother, as even the best behaved of boys got their arses walloped at one stage or the other. There was no such thing as because you had been out of trouble for so many weeks, that you wouldn't get the cane. Do the slightest thing wrong and you were for it and that was that. So to me it was a matter of 'balls to them', I would do what I wanted and let them do what they wanted. They were not going to break me, or what spirit I had. They came very close to doing so one or two times, but I always had the feeling that, from the way they treated kids, I was better than them. I wondered how they would cope with someone of their own size. But at the end of the day this was an approved school so all that went on in it must be approved too.

Meal times were a thing on their own. With each table having its own leader, most of the food went to those doing the leading. Each table would have a plate of bread and marge in the centre of it. There would also be a dish of jam or marmalade, supposedly to be shared out amongst the nine boys at each table. In practice this didn't work, the leaders thinking that they had the right to take the lion's share of whatever was on offer, to share between them and their mates.

Mick and I used to sit at the same table and, like all the other boys, just went along with things, but after our set-to with the house captain that changed. The very first meal after our difference with the captain happened to be breakfast. As soon as the two of us sat down at the table, and without waiting for the leader to grab his lion's share as was the usual way of things, we got stuck straight into the bread and so on already on the table. The leader did not say one word, not even when the other boys on the table also steamed into the food without his say so. From that day we all got our fair whack of what was going. No more, at least on the table I sat on, was it going to be that the strongest or best fighters ate what and how much they liked while the weaker got the scraps that were left.

The main course meals were served from a hotplate, at which we all had to queue. At lunch times, for example, we would line up to collect our food. Once the main course was over the queue would form again to collect the sweet of the day, taking with you the dirty main course plate. Things really livened up then. If for some reason you had not eaten any part of the main course you were not asked why, nor could you scrape it off the plate into a waste bin. What would happen is your sweet would be tipped on top of whatever you had left. So if you left cabbage - and how many kids liked that? - you would have, say, rice pudding poured over the top of it, and made to eat it, or six of the best. Of course, unless you were stupid, there was no way that you would take your main course plate back with anything on it. If you didn't like cabbage then stick it in your trouser pocket and throw it away when it was playtime, the same with any other food, like swede, that you may not have liked. There were quite a few boys in that school that had the continuous smell of cabbage on them!

The leader at the table that I sat at was a bit of a rat, he was always sneaking off to masters to report boys for the slightest thing, and would seem to delight in getting another kid punished. For small infringements the punishment was usually to have to stand to attention in the centre of the playground during the length of the play period. This could last for up to an hour. If you moved it cost you another session in the middle of the yard. Another punishment was carried out on Saturday nights only. Each Saturday evening a film would be shown in the dining room. As each boy filed into the dining room to take his seat for the film show, the headmaster's wife would issue out the weekly sweet ration, usually boiled sweets. All the sweets would be loose in a big bowl. As each boy filed past her, she would dip both her hands into the bowl and scoop up a double handful. Then looking at the boy about to be served, and seeing that yes, this one was alright, he would get both handfuls of the sweets; but if for some reason she did not like you, her hands would open up and half the sweets would fall back into the bowl.

The punishment that would be doled out on Saturday nights

would be as follows. The boy to be punished had to queue up for the film and his sweet ration, the same as everyone else. Once he had reached the headmaster's wife, she would tell him, 'No sweets for you.' He would then have to go out into the corridor, and there sit on the stone floor with hands on knees in an upright position as though sitting to attention, with his back to the dining room so he could hear - but not see - the film. The boy being punished may well know that he was to be so, so the point in making him go through all the queueing for sweets was just to prolong his punishment.

There were occasions when boys did not know they were to be punished, that is until they held their hands out for their sweet ration and then they would be told. This to me was the worst punishment of the two. There the boy would stand, in anticipation of sitting down to a film show with a handful of sweets, to be told right at the very last minute that he had nothing.

At times there could be as many as six or seven boys sitting to attention on the floor outside while the film show took place, some knowing what they had done, others not. The soundtrack of the film could be easily heard, as could the voices of the boys watching it, raised to give the hero warning of, 'Look behind you!' when he was being stalked by the villain. We would know by the music as the tension mounted in the film. On the times I sat there in that corridor, and hearing the shout of, 'Look behind you!' I was tempted to do just that. But I knew that if I did I would get a smack round the head by the master who would be there sitting in a nice easy chair, waiting and watching for one of us to look behind.

Caning took two forms; there was six or twelve across the arse, or four whacks across the palms of the hands with the same swishy cane. I'd had this arse-whacking bit on more than one occasion, every boy in the school had at one time or other, but I had never been struck across the palm. The master dealing this out had it off to a fine art; the cane would swish down from way above his head and then whack, straight across the tips of the fingers. Each of the four blows to each hand would hit exactly the same spot. Finger tips would swell to twice their proper size, and it would take a day or two for the swellings to go down enough so as to hold a pen or pencil in the classroom. All masters had the same art with that form of punishment. Strangely enough I had never seen or heard of the headmaster caning anyone on the hands. His particular sport was belting arses with his cane. While every master could cane a boy across the hands, only the head could do so across the arse. Perhaps with caning the hands he had to look you straight in the eye, and he didn't like the idea of that.

Back to our table leader. In spite of the fact that we had now got him under control, so that he did not take the lion's share of the food, he was still sneaking to the masters, and got boys into trouble, so Mick and I decided to teach him another lesson. One tea time we got our own back on him.

This leader was a glutton for jam sandwiches. Mick and I had been out in the grounds, taking a chance of being caught out of bounds, and we had dug up a long fat juicy worm, taking it into the dining room with us at tea time. Sitting at the table watching him spread two slices of bread and marge, and then covering it thickly with more than his share of jam, we said nothing, although some of the other kids were looking enquiringly at us as much as to say, 'Why are you letting him do this?' Once he had his sandwich made, we had to distract his attention. We did this by knocking the pot of tea in the centre of the table over in his direction. He leaped up from his chair, turning away from us to call out to one of the masters to show him what we had done. As quick as a flash out came the worm from Mick's snotty hanky, and into the jam sandwich it went. Over came the master to see what was going on, both Mick and I getting into trouble for knocking the pot over, and being told that we would have to stand in the middle of the yard during the next play session. But we were not too worried about that!

The table settled down and we began to eat our tea, but all eyes were on the leader, as everyone had seen what we had done. Picking up the jam sandwich, the leader took a huge bite out of it, hardly chewing it. Down it went in one swallow. It was after he took his second bite that I said to him, 'What's that in your sandwich?'

'Jam,' he replied.

'Not that,' I told him, 'I know it's jam but I thought I saw something move.'

Automatically he opened the sandwich up, and there was the second half of the worm without a wriggle in it. Jumping to his feet he shouted out, 'Sir!' as he did so throwing the remainder of the sandwich to the floor, and at the same time spitting what he had left onto the table. 'Sir' came over at a fair old clip as there was a sound of terror in the leader's voice, the rest of us around the table sitting there laughing our heads off. The leader by this time was bawling his eyes out.

Around us, from other tables, the shouts went up, 'What's happened?'

The master raised his voice and shouted, 'Everyone shut up!' and then asked the leader what had happened.

Sobbing, the boy said, 'Someone has put a worm in my jam sandwich.' With that the whole of the dining room erupted into laughter.

The end result was the master saying, 'Piper, Cowans, outside.'

So began the enquiry into the worm sandwich. Of course we denied all knowledge of it, and as there was on this occasion no sneaking, the whole matter was dropped. It was worth a play period standing in the middle of the yard for knocking the tea over. At last the worm had turned!

Hearing no more from the masters was one thing, but with the leaders of the tables, plus the house and vice-captain, it was a different matter. Having already upset the house captain, and in spite of the fact that he had not been so nasty since the night Mick and I had run away, he and the others decided to do something about Mick and myself. Some of the other kids were now waking up to the idea that these leaders were not all they were cracked up to be, and were doing things that they would not have done before Mick and I upset the apple cart. Now the leaders, captain and vice-captain were going to do something about Mick and I. We heard from a couple of the kids that this mob were out to get us, and intended to do so that night after lights out. Having been told this we became as determined to get them as they us.

We made our way early to the dorm, something we should not have done as dormitories were out of bounds until bedtime, but we wanted to plot up on them and take them by surprise, our intention being to jump them as soon as they entered the dorm. Having this in mind we armed ourselves with a heavy piece of wood each. We hid behind the dormitory door and waited. Whoever came through that door first was going to get a lump of wood over his nut. Of course that only meant the leaders as we had no intention to wallop any of the other boys. So we waited. As it happened, the first one to come to the dorm was the vice-captain. He pranced in, full of himself, but came back to earth with a thump when the first whack with the wood hit him straight on top of the nut. I don't remember who hit him first, but that didn't matter. His screams fetched others running, including one or two of the leaders. As soon as they saw what was happening they tried to get back out of the dorm, no doubt to fetch a master, but we were on them like a shot, our lumps of wood striking out now with no thought to who was being hit. There was now so much shouting and hollering going on it was sure to fetch a master, and so it did; not just one, there were two or three of them. By this time Mick and I had lost complete control of ourselves, and were still hitting out as masters swarmed all over us. At one point I didn't even realise it was a master who had got a grip of me from behind. Struggling like mad to break the grip on me, I raised the bit of wood to hit out when I noticed the pop-eyed master who had hold of me. Once the masters had gained control, we were all locked in the dormitory, friend and enemy alike, which seemed a bit up the pole to me.

It was not long before Mick and I were called to the head's office where yes, we were given twelve of the best. But the soreness of that wore off when we got to know that all the leaders had got six of the best, and lost their badges of office. So far as we were concerned we were the victors. Better still, there was no one in charge of the dorm now, we were all on the same level, which is just how it should be. We got enough old bollocks and rules and regulations from the masters without getting it from some of the boys as well. It wasn't too long either before those of the boys who had lost their authority came round to our way of doing things. Their attitude being that Mick and I had started the fight and, as they had done nothing, they should not have been punished. They too now had the hump with the masters, which was a bit off to me, as if they hadn't said that they were going to get Mick and me then the fight wouldn't have started!

None of that was any concern now though. From Allenby being the best house in the school it now became the worst. At one time we were proud of the fact that through our behaviour we had reached the dizzy heights of three months without lights. The only problem we had in our dorm was that so many boys were getting caned. We had even given up the habit of looking at a boy's arse after a caning; if we had continued to do that we would have spent half our lives looking at badly-bruised arses.

Now we were doing what we wanted, when we wanted, with only one common enemy - the masters. Now we were all working together, we were skylarking about at night after lights out. We had a spy system set up, each taking turns, one boy standing outside the dorm door, with another at the top of the stairs as first guard. One evening we had two boys keeping watch as usual. The boy who had top-of-the-stairs duty was called Foghorn, and that was just what his voice sounded like. The call that would go up from him to the boy at the door who would pass it on to all of us was 'Nitto!' When that call sounded then a master was on his way. On this night Foghorn was on guard duty. He gave the yell of, 'Nitto!' Quickly we all jumped into bed, and all appeared to be sleeping the sleep of the innocent. Suddenly the lights were switched on, a voice bellowed out, 'Nitto, no lights for two nights!' Yes, the master had heard Foghorn, and so I should think had the rest of Sussex. That was the last time Foghorn was used as a lookout.

The staff had their own dining room, the school matron being in charge of it. She used to lay the tables for them and generally look after it. Each master had his own chair at the table, and with rationing still being in force, each place setting had little pots of butter, jam and so on at them. Stuck on the table in front of each of the chairs was a small flag, so that everyone was aware of who sat where, and whose pot of jam or butter was laid out before them. Once a week the matron would bake a huge currant cake for the masters which she used to put in a tin in the staff dining room each Saturday, ready for high tea for all of the masters on Sunday. Becoming aware of this we set out to raid the dining room one Saturday night. With this in mind, on the Saturday that the raid was to take place we were all on our best behaviour.

Going to bed and appearing to settle down early, there was no horse play or any of the usual larking about. Of course we spoke to each other in whispers, we had to or we would have fallen asleep. We were waiting for the night watchman to make his usual rounds before we made our move. Round he came and did his usual karzi karzi bit with the piss-the-beds, but this night there was a difference; as he shook the shoulder of the first piss-the-bed all of them got out of bed together, and all went to the karzi at the same time. This was part of our plan as we did not want any delay. The night watchman stood back in amazement at this sudden exodus of piss-the-beds and was heard to mutter, 'What the hell's going on?' Soon things settled down once again and Mick and I were ready to go and nick the cake. Any raids, no matter on what, always seemed to be done by Mick and myself, and if anyone was going to be caught it always seemed to be Mick!

Anyway, off we both set leaving the dorm by the usual route - the fire escape. Once in the grounds we had to make our way to the other side of the school, to get to the window that would get us into the masters' dining room. There was plenty of cover, through trees and bushes, so we arrived safely. Once there, we had no problem in getting the window open and climbing in, then drawing the curtains and switching on the light. There before us was the table all laid out with its pots of jam and so on, with the little flags with the masters' names on them. There were even small blocks of cheese, but we were not interested in that for the moment, we had come for the cake!

Opening the cupboard where it was kept, we had to take a second look, as what was this? There were two cake tins. Taking them both from the cupboard, we were in for a disappointment; there were not two cakes, just the one, the other tin being full of biscuits. But, oh well, we would take them too! Stuffing the cake and biscuits into an old bag we had with us, we then went round the table taking a piece of cheese, and pots of jam and marmalade from the places of those we thought to be the worst of the masters. Unfortunately the headmaster did not have a spot in this dining room, he ate in his quarters with his family, unfortunate in so much as we would have nicked every bit of his grub if it had been available. But our final bit of food to nick sat on top of the sideboard: a loaf of bread.

Getting back to the dormitory was as easy as getting to the dining room. Once back everything was shared out as far as it would go. Then, completely full up of cake, bread and jam, with a few biscuits to round off our feast, we settled down for the night happy. The following day we were all puzzled as to why nothing was said about the missing cake and food. It was a bit of a relief too as we had expected Olive Oil and his cronies to cane the whole school.

As Allenby, the house I was in, didn't have any leaders or house captain, the masters had more to do as they now had to look after the running of Allenby instead of leaving it to the house captain or vice-captain. The masters did not like this at all as it took away their easy life of dossing around with no one now to do their lackying for them. House meetings were held once a week, and once a week it was raised by the house master that we should elect new leaders. Then it would be, 'Right, any boy or boys who would like to propose anyone for these privileged positions, raise their hands.' Not a hand was raised. The masters even threatened to pick one of us for the job of house captain if we didn't do so, but we knew that they wouldn't do that as we knew (and so did they) that this would not work.

Of course, always being the worst house at the school meant that it was always us who got the dirty jobs when it came to the cleaning. We would find ourselves cleaning the toilets each day, emptying bins and so on.

Even though we had to do most of the dirty work, we had our compensations. We all did what we liked when we liked, with no bully to stop us or run to the masters with tales. There became a kind of comradeship between us - we were all sticking together. If anyone was caught or found out to be sneaking to any of the masters then the whole dorm would be up in arms. It even came to the point that if we had a vacancy in our dorm, kids from other dorms would ask for a change to where we were. Of course this was only the boys who were always in trouble, none of the well-behaved wanted to come in with us. Strangely enough, the masters used to agree to these moves quite readily. Perhaps they thought it was best to keep all the rotten apples in one place - I quite enjoyed being considered a rotten apple. The boys who did misbehave in other dorms, who led lives of misery being bullied, were to join us. A peculiar situation altogether; in any of the other dorms boys would be bullied if they misbehaved, whilst in Allenby they would be bullied if they didn't misbehave!

Once a week, in the dining room, the headmaster would announce the results of the points for good and bad behaviour, who was top boy and so on. There he would stand in front of us all, and in his squeaky voice would say, 'I'm happy to tell you that this week's house winners are Haig.' Cheering from the mob from

Haig, with polite clapping from the runners up Jellicoe, a little bit less applause from Beattie coming third, and a stony silence from Allenby who didn't give a shit. Then the headmaster would announce, 'And as usual Allenby are last, and a disgrace to the school.'

But back to skullduggery. For three weeks on the trot we went to the masters' dining room and nicked the cake. With each week's success, the more we wondered as to how stupid the masters were to keep leaving it in the same place; as long as they did we were only too happy to nick it. Mick and I had now set up a routine whereby if something had to be done we would take turns each to do it, while the other one kept watch. So it came to the fourth night, and, as usual on a Saturday, off we set to nick the cake. On this occasion it was Mick's turn to get in the window and then pass the cake out to me. Nothing had changed, it was still easy to get into the masters' dining room. I gave Mick a lift up to the window sill, up went the window and in went Mick feet first. Suddenly Mick let out the most horrifying scream that I had so far heard in my life. All thoughts of the delicious fruit cake flew from my mind. Mick was on the window sill trying to pull himself away from the monster that had a grip on him. The only sounds were from Mick who was gradually disappearing through the window, being dragged by whatever, until he eventually went from sight. Still rooted to the spot and unable to speak, I watched a massive dark shape appear in the window through which Mick had disappeared. The sight of this hulk gave me life - I took off like a bat out of hell. There was no thought of dodging through the bushes and trees to secretly get back to the dorm; now it was a panic-stricken run!

As I burst through the fire escape door back into the dorm there were shouts of, 'What's going on Ron?' Me, well I just jumped straight into bed without giving any answer and covered my head with the covers, shaking with fear.

Ages later something touched my shoulder. I gave a little scream and leapt from my bed. There standing by my side was a master who grabbed my arm, with a look of shock on his face at my scream, so much so that he screamed back at me, 'You get yourself down to the headmaster's study right now!' So down there I went, and there was Mick standing facing the wall, the usual procedure while waiting for the head to deal with you. Out came the headmaster. I was questioned as to what I had been doing.

'Sleeping,' I told him.

'You're a horrible little liar,' he told me, 'you've been with Cowans stealing from the masters' dining room.'

'Not me sir, I've been in bed asleep,' was the only answer I could give him.

His answer to that was, 'Well now you can watch this.'

Mick was made to take up the caning position, and off went the head for his run up before delivering the first whack across Mick's arse, and on through until the six of the best was complete. Perhaps the head thought that the actual caning being watched by me would be a cure for me to behave myself. If he did think that way then he was very wrong. Looking at him running towards the bent over Mick gave me a clear look at his face. It wasn't a pretty sight. He seemed to be relishing what he was about to do. This was in a way confirmed by his actions after the six lashes were over. Mick stood up and began to walk away. The head let him get five or six paces then called out, 'Come back here Cowans, I've not finished with you. You have another six to come for not telling me who was with you.' I felt sick at this, how could anyone do this? The action of that headmaster was, and still is, one of the cruellest things I have ever seen. The act of letting someone believe the punishment was over only to start again, in itself taught me to think, 'Fuck these people who have been approved to run this approved school. They are not going to win!'

As yet in my short life I had not learnt to hate anyone; dislike yes, hate no. I didn't even know what hate felt like, but I learnt that night. I hated that fat bastard so much, and today, thinking back on that night, I know the hate is still there.

If I had been big enough I would have taken the cane away from him and beaten him around the face with it. Mick didn't cry or flinch while the caning was taking place, even through the second part of it. When it was over we both stood and looked at the head for a second or two, and then walked away with our arms round each others' shoulders. Usually we would have been told to run, but on this night there must have been a feeling in the air from us to him because he said nothing.

Once we were out of his sight we both cried, but we pulled ourselves together before we went back into the dorm. There was no way we were going to let any of the others see our tears. Once there we went straight to bed, without talking to anyone. I'm sure that if anyone had asked to look at Mick's arse that night we would have beaten them to death. Thankfully they didn't, and from that night the practice ceased altogether. A bond was formed between Mick and myself that was to last all our time together at Mile Oak, and in thoughts when we parted. But we were, if nothing else, resilient, and we were soon back at what we knew best. Only this time we were heading for the headmaster.

As I've said earlier, every Saturday there was a film show and the issuing of sweet rations. One time I had joined this queue to see the film and get my sweets, only to find on reaching the head's wife that I was on punishment. She had actually tipped a few of the sweets into my hand when she told me to put them back and to go to the corridor. I threw the sweets back into the bowl and shouted at her, 'Stick 'em up your arse!' With that I was dragged by the scruff of the neck to the head's office.

This offence was to be twelve of the best, which was carried out (if at all possible) with a bit of extra venom, and a lot of muttering from the head of, 'How dare you talk to my wife like that.' I was then made, as usual, to sit on the stone floor in the corridor through the film show. Not very comfortable with my arse on fire, but the cold floor soon took the heat out of it.

But back to our heading for the headmaster. Each week the sweets were delivered to the school by someone from the local shop. This was normally in the early part of the week. They were taken to the headmaster's office, where they were kept until the day of issue. Now, his office looked out over the playground, the window that did so was only a few feet off of the ground and easily reached. This was to be our target. We were going to nick those sweets no matter what. It actually turned out to be a lot easier than we thought it might be. We had to rope in another couple of kids to help us cart the sweets off.

We waited several nights before getting on with the job, talking all the time about how we were going to do it. I feel sure now that we were more nervous over getting into the head's office than we were about anything we had done so far. Why this should be I don't know, as the worst that could happen to us would be to get twelve of the best if caught, and that didn't bother us too much. But his office had to be got into and the sweets nicked. As

I've said, it was all so simple. Getting to the window in the playground and into the office was as easy as walking through the door. Mick and I got in, and there before us were the sweets. Whatever doubt we had had about doing this now disappeared. Quickly grabbing boxes of sweets we passed them out to the two boys waiting outside. By the time we had finished there was not a sweet left in the office. Getting back to the dorm with our prize was as easy as having left it in the first place.

On this night there was not one boy asleep. They were all sitting up in bed smacking their lips in anticipation. In a short while all the sweets were shared out. Boys began to disappear in all directions to hide part of their shares away, keeping some back to scoff before falling into a contented sleep. The following day there was uproar, the theft having been discovered fairly early in the day, which was a surprise really as the head didn't usually go to his office until late in the morning, but here it was, still breakfast time. All of us were contently eating our breakfast when in walked the headmaster, something he had never done before. The whole school was made to stop eating and all stand. Then the lecture began.

'Someone has broken into my office during the night and has stolen the entire sweet ration for the school. Now I want those sweets returned. I do not expect the cowardly person or persons to own up to this theft, but I will be giving everyone the opportunity to leave the sweets where they can be easily found. If they are, then there will be no need to punish the whole school. Has anyone anything to say on this matter?'

No one did except for one lunatic of a boy from Haig house who put his hand up. The head spotting the boy's hand looked over at him with a bit of a smile on his face and said, 'Well what have you got to say?'

The smile quickly disappeared from the head's face when the boy enquired, 'Sir if someone has nicked all the sweets, does that mean we will get no sweet ration this week?'

The headmaster just stared at this boy without saying a word. So long and hard did he stare at him that the boy sank to his feet, probably in dread as to what was going to happen to him. Thankfully for him nothing did, the head being otherwise engaged in his thoughts. We were then told that there would be no classes that morning, that we should all go to our dorms until lunch time, where the culprits could decide whether to put the sweets in a place where they could be recovered. The headmaster even suggested that they be left in the playground, with the promise that no one would be watching. 'What a lot of old cobblers,' I thought to myself.

Back in the dorm all that we discussed in Allenby was: 'Had everyone hid their sweets well?' We all had. I do not think that the masters did any searching, they certainly did not search any of the dorms.

Come lunch time we were all called back to the dining room, where we were in for another talking to by the headmaster, who had this to say, 'Just as I expected, none of the sweets have been recovered. The whole school will have no playground activities. At each play period you will all parade in the yard in house order and there you will stay until bedtime. Once it is time to go to your dormitories, you will all go straight to bed, lights will be turned out immediately. This punishment will last for a week. There will also be no film show on Saturday and no sweets for anyone this week.'

So that was the end of that lecture. Most of the punishments that we had been given didn't bother anyone in Allenby, as we were, if not all of us, quite a few, already on one. There was a lot of muttering from other houses that they knew who did it and so on, but none of them were prepared to do a thing about it, as they knew only too well that those of us in Allenby were staunch and would all stick together if any of them started any trouble.

One thing that those in Haig, Beattie and Jellicoe tried was to put all of us in Allenby into coventry, but we didn't give a shit about that as we did not want them talking to us anyway. As for the lights out for a week, that was no sweat as we never took too much notice of that as nearly all our best times were after dark.

There was one master in the school that everyone was wary of. His nickname for some reason or other was Bomber. Why, I don't know, even the other masters called him by that name. To my mind, and having tasted some of it, his form of punishment was the most painful to the receiver. Bomber did not believe in the cane in any shape or form. The way he meted out punishment was to make the offending boy sit cross-legged on the floor. Then he would have to pull his shorts up to the top of his thighs, then place his hands and arms behind his back, leaning backwards onto them. In this position the inside of the boy's thighs would stand out clearly. Bomber would stand above the boy then raise his hand high above his head. Then with a quick swoop downwards, would smash the boy across the inside of the thigh with the palm of his hand. This he would do four times on each thigh. The shock of his palm smashing the thigh gave one a sickening feeling, the pain of it is hard to describe. When Bomber was giving out this sort of treatment, it would take a long time, as with each smack of the palm across the thigh, the boy being punished rolled over in agony. And with eight smacks in all to come, and the thought of the rest after the first one, every boy I knew tried to prolong the punishment with the thought that if they did so the pain would not be so bad between smacks. But that was a false feeling. Bomber would wait patiently for the boy to sit back up, as if he had all the time in the world and nothing better to do. Perhaps he hadn't.

One good thing came of the disappearing sweets; for once Allenby were not the lone worst house in the school. We were joined by all the rest of them, and they suffered more than us. We were used to it but they weren't. Perhaps that's a cock-eyed way of looking at things, seeing that we in Allenby were the culprits, but what the hell! It was the way we saw things. Somewhere along the line Mick and myself seemed to be getting more stick than most, as it didn't matter what we were doing, we got pulled up. If we went to the toilet a master would shortly follow us and ask what we were up to. If we were just idling in the yard, leaning against a wall, up someone would come and say, 'What are you two up to? Move along.' But really we didn't mind, as it now seemed if we were doing nothing it appeared to aggravate the masters. All good stuff! Things soon settled down though, and from being careful we steered away from bother. It was boring, but had to be done.

Once the week of punishment was over for the whole school, things soon got back to normal, and so did Mick and me. Our next escapade was to sneak over to the farm late at night and steal some potatoes, for baking in the boiler house. Our mission to the farm was a success, and we were soon in the boiler house baking jacket potatoes. The boiler house had two boilers in it, one of which was always alight. The potatoes we would put on a large coal shovel and then into the furnace. We were getting along quite happily, and had quite a few potatoes ready, with not too many left to bake when suddenly we heard a snuffling sound at the door, then the rattling of keys. Someone was about to enter. Of course we made our exit through a window. Mick and I both made dives in different directions. I ran to the empty furnace and pulling the fire door open jumped in, pulling the door to after me, leaving it open slightly so that I could see who was coming in. God knows what Mick thought he was doing as he appeared to be trying to bury himself under a ton of coal heaped up in one corner of the boiler house. Before he was able to do that the door opened and there stood the headmaster with his little Scottie dog, but swinging the dog's leash through the air. Spotting Mick covered in coal dust he began to lash out at him with the leash, all the time shouting at him to report outside his office straight away.

The headmaster began to call out, 'Come out Ron Piper, I know you are in here somewhere.' But I thought sod that for a lark! There was no way that I was going to declare myself.

He soon got fed up calling my name and left, locking the boiler house behind him. As soon as I felt it was safe, which was within seconds, I was out of that boiler house as quick as I could go, and back to the safety of my bed in the dorm. But the safety aspect of it did not last for long. Hardly having tucked myself between the sheets, than I was being woken from my pretend sleep by one of the masters, and told to report to the head's office.

Once again there was Mick standing facing the wall with the head prancing up and down swishing his beloved cane. As always I was questioned as to where I had been. Again I told of how I was in bed asleep. Then the usual happened; Mick had to take up the position for six of the best and I had to watch. When that was over, Mick and I began to walk away. Again we were called back, only this time it was me the headmaster spoke to.

'So Piper, you haven't been down to the boiler room with Cowans?'

'No sir,' was my reply to that.

'Well, well, well,' said the head, 'In that case you can have six of the best for going to bed in the filthy condition you are in, and perhaps that will teach you to wash before you go to bed in future.' So there we are, this time things evened out. Back in the dorm I went to to the toilet and looked at myself in the mirror - I was covered in dirt from the boiler.

Mick and I now decided to have another go at running away, only this time we were not going to take any chances by falling asleep on the train. We were going to hitchhike, and we intended to go in the dead of night. We waited for the night watchman to do his second round of Karzi Karzi with the piss-the-beds one Saturday night, and off we set. Down the fire escape and away. Crossing a field close to the school feeling quite happy with ourselves, that is until the heavens opened up and it began to piss down with rain, with nowhere in sight to shelter. Between us we decided to go back and wait for the rain to stop, and if it didn't, set out again the following night.

Making our way back, and just as we were about to climb the stairs of the fire escape, a voice shouted out, 'Right you two, stay there!' Knowing that it was too dark for anyone to see who we were, we took off up the fire escape. Half way up, and now with footsteps close behind, Mick decided to fall 'arse over head' back down the stairs, and straight into the arms of our pursuer. I ran on and back into the dorm, but I was soaking wet and there was no way I was going to jump into bed wet and fully clothed. I had learnt my lesson from the boiler house episode. So grabbing my pyjamas on the way past my bed, I headed for the toilet to clean myself up as quick as I could. But the unusual happened. The master that had caught Mick did not take him straight to the head's office. He brought him up into the dorm from the fire escape, as I later found out, and spotting my bed empty began to call out, 'Piper, Piper, where are you?' The bastard thought he had me.

From the toilet I called back, 'In here.'

'What are you doing in there?' he shouted back.

Fancy asking someone that who was in the toilet, I thought to myself as I shouted back, 'Having a shit!'

'Well as soon as you have finished report to the headmaster's office,' was his reply to that.

So here we are again I thought. Mick this time got twelve of the best with me watching, and I got twelve of the best for having a shit! The headmaster made it quite clear that he knew I was with Mick, but as I hadn't been caught, I was to be punished for using such language. I suppose one reason for being caned is as good as another. Evidently I should have called out I was having a 'number two'. Now I have never heard such a lot of old cobblers in my life; number one for a piss and number two for a shit, what on earth next? I could just imagine saying to my mother, 'I'm going for a number two.' She would have wondered what the hell was going on!

good old Sussex by the sea

IT WAS THE PRACTICE AT THE SCHOOL for there to be home leaves at Easter, mid-term, and Christmas. The only problem being that parents had to send the fares. Coming up to these holiday periods, daily lists were made up and displayed on a notice board. These lists were usually put up just before lunch, so as soon as classes ended for the morning there would be a rush to see if your name was on the list. There were two attitudes each day to the lists: pure delight on the faces of those who had their names on the list, and a sadness on those who didn't. I had been at Mile Oak for quite a while now, and several holidays had come and gone without my name being on the list. But I still had not got used to the idea that it was not, and still ran to have a look each time a new list was put up, to see if my name was on it. Mick wasn't the only orphan at the school, there were one or two others, and they, along with Mick, would all run along to the notice board each lunch time. Mick would always be telling me that his mum and dad would send his fare this time. I had given up trying to explain to him that he had no parents. So each day he waited for the miracle to happen.

Looking back on it all I suppose it was a comforting thought for him to dream that one day his parents would find him, or him they. But really I don't know who was the saddest: those with parents who never sent the fares for their kids, so couldn't care less, or those with no parents who knew in their heart of hearts that their fare would not come. Perhaps saddest of all was the hope of the boys who did have parents, as they never gave up hope with them. If their fares did not come so they could go home at Easter they would say, 'My mum will send it for mid-term,' and so on.

On my second Christmas at the school, as I had done on all the previous holidays that had come and gone I looked at the list - and there it was, my name was on the list. I couldn't wait to get away from the notice board and find Mick so I could tell him my news. When I found him and shouted, 'Mick, I'm going home for Christmas, my name's on the list!' he just looked at me and walked away, a thing he had never done in the past. I chased after him and jumped in front of him to stop him, saying to him, 'What's up?' He was crying and couldn't speak to me. A terrible sadness came over me, and I told him that I wouldn't go, that I would take him with me, even though I knew I couldn't. There wasn't much I could say to him, so I shut up. We just walked together out of the school buildings and out of bounds. We didn't give a shit if we got caught and got the cane. We just wanted to be together, and fuck the masters and their rules and regulations. We went out into the fields and just sat there, not saying much to each other really. There was no point in talking.

It seemed like hours that we sat out there, eventually going back into the school. Yes, we were caught and sent to the headmaster's office. We knew it was twelve of the best for being out of bounds, but so bloody what! But we were in for a surprise when out came Olive Oil swishing his cane. Suddenly he stopped, and staring at us asked, 'What were you doing out of bounds?' Now we were never ever asked anything like that. If rules of any sort were broken it was straight on with the punishment with no chance of giving an excuse. Perhaps on this occasion he saw something in our faces. Looking up at him in surprise, I shouted, 'I'm going home for Christmas and Mick isn't, and it ain't bloody fair.'

With that the headmaster took us into his office, a place we had never been invited into before. In fact the only time I had been in there was the day I arrived, and the night Mick and I had nicked the sweets. Now he sat us down and tried to explain to us why Mick couldn't go home, but we just sat there and said nothing, still expecting to get caned. Suddenly the headmaster stood up and going to a cupboard pulled out a box of sweets and gave us a handful each. Then he told us to go to the dining room for our meal, and to behave ourselves.

Although we did not appreciate it at the time, that was the kindest act he had done us two, but later that was to fall a bit flat. Came the day that the Christmas leave was to start, Mick and I were reluctant to part. His last words to me when we had to separate were, 'You will come back, won't you?'

We were going to walk to the station, and it was in the usual crocodile line of walking along in twos. Once on the train I sat on my own. I didn't feel like talking to anyone. Of course all the others were full of excitement. We had to change trains at

Brighton, which fetched back the memory of when Mick and I had run away and fell asleep on the train, to be caught and taken back to Mile Oak. Four masters were with us on the journey to Victoria where our parents were to pick us up. One of the masters was also the music teacher at the school. Although there was a choir at Mile Oak I had never seen anyone being taught music. But there he was on the train with us and he wanted us to sing. This was evacuation all over again, only this time it was not 'It's a Hap Hap Happy Day' that we had to sing (which on this occasion would have been more appropriate), now it was 'Sussex by the Sea, Good old Sussex by the Sea'. Was I never ever going to get away from cranks who wanted me and others like me to sing the most oddball songs? But there we were, a group of boys all from London singing about Sussex, when most of us, being at Mile Oak and getting away from it for a while, were thinking, 'Fuck Sussex!'

Eventually we arrived at Victoria, and as the train was pulling into the station windows were being opened and heads craning out to look for parents who should be waiting. Masters were screaming out, 'Don't open the doors before the train stops!' They had no chance of being obeyed. As the train pulled slowly into the platform, doors were flung open and boys leaped from the still moving train, with masters leaping out after us calling out, 'Everybody stop here.' Which we did, not because they had called out, but because there was not a parent in sight. Once order was restored we were formed back into a crocodile and marched up to the ticket barrier.

There the parents were. Boys were now shouting and pointing, 'There's my mum,' or, 'There's my dad,' and so on. I looked around for my mother but couldn't see her anywhere. After a while of looking about I spotted my grandfather. The ticket barrier was opened and parents, or whoever, were allowed onto the platform to gather their kids. I was a bit disappointed that my mother wasn't there to collect me, so much so that I didn't greet my grandfather except to ask, 'Where's my mum?' to be told that she was at work.

Being back in London and back in the old district felt strange, as if I didn't belong there anymore. Everything was so different, even the streets seemed different. The bombed houses had been shored up and appeared to be more secure than they used to be. The war was in its closing stages, the end of it passing me by while

I had been away. The fun of the streets had disappeared with it. I was now coming up to fourteen. The games that I used to play now seemed to be too juvenile to take part in. All the old gangs of kids were still about, nearly all returned from evacuation, but now there did not seem to be gangs as such, it was all a matter of just having mates.

The Yanks, although still around were less in number, and there appeared to be more British soldiers around. My brother and my old mate Dave were also on leave from their approved schools. Together we just wandered aimlessly around the streets. The week's leave we had did not seem long enough for us to get back onto our old footing. It was as though we were strangers. The excitement of looting and nicking lead had gone. Even getting our revenge on Chocolate Joe had been put to the back of our minds, although we still owed him a thing or two. Even though my brother, Dave and myself still drifted about together, we had nothing to do with any of the old gang. To us they still seemed to be kids and we had outgrown them, even if they were the same age. There was too the feeling that they had been told by their parents not to associate with us, one boy even telling us this. According to him we were trouble. If only their parents had known that we didn't want to play with their kids. Our playing days were over.

My mind was still back at Mile Oak. As much as I hated the place and the people who ran it, in an odd sort of way I missed it. There was a sort of comradeship there that wasn't in the streets I knew so well. The time couldn't come quick enough for me to get back on the train even if it meant singing 'Sussex by the Sea'. But time dragged by with no sense of purpose. I wished Mick was with me, I knew that if that had been possible I would not have wanted to go back, as we could have been together in the streets. I could have shown him things we could have done together.

I still had to get him a Christmas present, but what? I hadn't a clue, until walking down one of the old streets and seeing in a hardware shop window a row of beautiful sheath knives. One of these would do, they were perfect. The only problem was they were far above anything that I could afford. But one of these knives was what I was going to get. I explained to my brother and Dave what I wanted one of these knives for, and that I intended to smash the shop window late at night and nick them. I asked them if they wanted to come with me. Dave was all for it but my brother said no.

With Dave I went back to the shop as soon as it was dark. With no messing about whatsoever, up to the window putting a brick through it, a quick grab at the knives and off we went. There were a few shouts from people passing by, but that was all. No one chased us. In all we had five knives, Dave and I taking two each, giving the odd one to my brother. That was one present, what else could I get? The only other thing that I could think of was sweets, I would get as many of them as I could. With every penny of money that I could lay my hands on, sweets were what I bought. Having no coupons I had to buy some on the black market, which was more expensive, but I didn't mind that.

The week that I had at home was now over and the day to go back to Mile Oak arrived. Other kids from schools in the area that I lived had three or four weeks off, but us at approved school had just the week, which was enough for me. It was left to my grandfather again to take me back to Victoria, to meet up with the rest of the boys going back and the masters who were there to meet us at the station. Once at the station I said a quick goodbye to my grandfather and I was away, amongst the rest of the boys. I headed straight for those who were in Allenby with me, but I appeared to be the only cheerful one on the station, all the other boys looking pretty glum at having to go back.

The train journey began, but what a difference, it was done in silence. Even with the music teacher being one of the masters who had met us at Victoria station, no songs were sung nor did he attempt to get any started. Back at Portslade station it was the crocodile walk back to the school. Everyone seemed to be going at funeral pace, which was getting on my nerves a bit.

Back at the school we all had to parade in the yard, while Olive Oil gave a welcome back speech, and hoped we had all enjoyed ourselves. All the rest of the boys who had not been home were standing around in the yard calling out to their particular friends, but there was no sign of Mick. There were shouts of, 'Did you bring any sweets back,' and so on, while on and on droned the headmaster. Why couldn't he shut his mouth and dismiss us so that I could go and find Mick? Eventually he did just that and off I went. Off into the house I ran calling Mick's name, getting no answer; perhaps he was in the dorm which he should not have been at this time of day, but that would not have worried Mick.

Once in the dorm the first thing that I noticed was that Mick's bed, which was next to mine, had been stripped. Looking quickly in the direction of the lockers I found that his locker was empty. The bastards had moved him to another dorm I thought. Running back down the stairs, I bumped straight into one of the masters. Before I could utter a word he asked, 'And what are you doing upstairs? Get out into the yard.'

'Never mind about that,' I told him, 'where's Mick Cowans?'

He just looked at me and said, 'Yard. You'll find out later where Cowans is.' So there was nothing else I could do but to go back to the yard where all the rest of the school were, all getting back together again with stories of what they had been doing on their holidays.

I stood in the yard by myself talking to no one. I fancied I was getting strange looks from one or two of the other boys from my house, but didn't think too much of it. Suddenly my name was called by one of the masters, and I was told by him to report to the headmaster's office.

Once there I was told by the head, 'Cowans has been moved to another school. We are all sick and tired of the disruptive influence you two have over other boys when you are together. Now get out.'

As I walked away I muttered to myself, 'Up yours Olive Oil.'

'What did you say?' he roared, but I never took a blind bit of notice of him and carried on walking. Unusually for him he let me go without calling me back.

All this time I had been carrying the carrier bag with the sweets and sheath knife in it that was for Mick. Out of the school grounds I walked, I was now out of bounds, but bollocks to the boundaries! I walked in the direction of a small woods. There I swung the carrier bag round my head a few times and then let it go. It sailed throught the air and landed somewhere amongst the trees and the bushes. There was nothing in it that I wanted, even my sheath knife. On the way back into the school grounds I got caught by the thigh slapper, so got the usual slaps across the inside of my thighs. Even that didn't hurt that much for once.

After my first day back I didn't mix with anyone. I just associated myself with anyone who was up to no good, which was an easy task as most of them were in Allenby with me still. I didn't worry too much about getting the cane or stuff like that.

I was coming up to fourteen now and I thought that they couldn't hold me in this place for much longer. This was a junior approved school, so one way or the other they would have to get rid of me, whether by sending me home or pushing me off to another school. I had no great concern as to what way they did it, just as long as they got me out of here. But there was still time to be got through.

I must have been getting to these people as I was being caned and slapped around the thighs so often that in the end it became a natural way of life. It came to the point in the end that the slapping and the caning stopped, and they ignored me. I didn't like that one little bit as ignoring people was my game, as I had found; ignore those in authority and they lost control of themselves. Now it was working in reverse, except that I did not lose control as they did. In the end I just floated along doing my own thing for weeks on end. Gradually I began to do as I was told, and in doing so I got to them again. I was looked at in disbelief. I was continually being asked what I was up to. On one occasion the thigh-slapper passed the remark, 'So you have been tamed at last.'

My reply to that was, 'Bollocks!' But still I wasn't punished for using bad language, so I felt, 'No, it isn't me that has been beaten, it's you you bastard.' My time at Mile Oak was coming to an end, but not in the way that I thought.

one of the idle rich

EASTER WAS UPON US and we were all going home again; or those of us who had their fares sent, me being one of them. The same old procedure took place getting to Victoria, the same song on the train. Looking back, I feel that when the boys of Mile Oak were on their way to London and sang 'Sussex by the Sea', it could not have been sung with any more fervour by people who were from Sussex on their way home. Once again I was met by my grandfather and was soon home. Home was still the same three rooms. I still had to share a bed with my brother in the kitchen. The bugs were still in the walls but I had now lost interest in squashing them. The pattern I had formed with the squashed bugs was still plain to see. One of the worst things of being home, I found, was having to share a bed. I had got so used to having my own space. My brother had been released from his approved school about a month before I came home for the Easter holiday. So too had my mate Dave, I was to find out later in the day.

The sleeping bit was just as bad as ever, with my mother and her cronies sitting together chatting for half the night. Of course my brother and I were now a lot bigger and wiser. Most of the talk that went on between my mother and her mates we now understood. When they told each other about some woman or other having it with some bloke, we knew exactly what they meant, which was a bit of an embarrassment to them as they now spoke in whispers. Or my mother would say, 'Ain't you going out?' and when we did, did not concern herself over what time we came back in, which suited me. Being fourteen, and my brother now sixteen, it was an embarrassment to us to try to go to bed when our bedroom was full of chattering women, some of whom, through the lack of space once our bed was down, would park their arses on our bed. Trying to sleep, if I did go to bed early, was impossible. There would be the continuous tea-making, and when any of the women had spare money there would be bottles of stout or brown ale drank by them.

Now most of the Yanks had gone back home, none of the women seemed to want to go out on weekend nights. I suppose that now most of them had husbands at home they could do that no longer.

But they could go on chatting to each other for hours on end. If I was in bed, that I could stand, but when they started to get sentimental that drove me up the wall with the bugs, as they began to sing all the old songs. They would take it in turns. My mother or someone would call out, 'Come on Doris, sing a song,' and off would go Doris, or Mary or Betty or whoever. Each of them had their favourites. What's more, none of them had a quiet singing voice. They would belt out the numbers at the top of their voices.

This Easter holiday was to be only for a few days, and on the second or third day my mother got a letter telling her that I did not have to go back to Mile Oak, and that I had been discharged. Enclosed were forms to the effect. She was also told that she had to take me to a place called County Hall where I would be given clothing.

The job of taking me to County Hall, which was a large building on the Embankment in London, was given to my grandfather. Once there he gave the forms, that my mother had been sent by the school, to a woman standing behind a counter. She stood there eyeing me up and down for a while, and then disappeared through a doorway behind her without saying a word. My grandfather and I stood and waited for her to come back for half an hour or so. On her re-appearance, in her arms she was carrying bundles of clothes that she passed to me: shirts, socks, a couple of jackets and so on. I tried the jackets on and they fitted me to a 't', but on unfolding the trousers she had given me, I found them to be shorts. There I stood in front of this woman in long trousers, and here she was giving me short trousers. Was she some sort of crank? Passing them back over the counter, I told her that I did not want these, that I wanted long trousers. All she replied to that was, 'We do not do long trousers.'

Now I was beginning to get the hump with her. Here I was, fourteen, had left school and was supposed to get a job. How the hell was I going to do that in short trousers? The ones I had on were the only pair of trousers that I had, and they were falling to bits. Then this pot-house of a woman said again, 'We do not do long trousers.'

What was she - a bloody parrot? Keep telling me the same thing. Now she had given me the hump, and I was just about to tell her to stick her shorts up her arse (after all she couldn't cane me,

I was free from all that now) when my grandfather butted in and said to her, 'Are you in charge or do you just work here? If you only work here, go and get someone who is in charge and with a bit more sense.' Now, to say this woman went off in a huff is to put it mildly.

I stood there mouth agape, as my grandfather was usually a quiet sort of feller, and this was the longest speech I had ever heard him make. As soon as I got over the shock of it we both stood there grinning at each other, my grandfather saying to me, 'Don't start getting rude Ron.'

Within a few minutes, back came this woman to tell me that I had to have some measurements taken. This was done and a short while later back she came with two pairs of grey flannel trousers, long ones. Where the hell she got them when she kept saying, 'We don't have long trousers here,' I don't know, but I now had them and that was good enough for me. We signed for what we had been given, or at least my grandfather did, and off we went home.

The next thing on the list was to get a job, which I did quite easily. It was with one of the local butchers, riding a bike about delivering meat to all the posh houses in Marylebone. When I wasn't out delivering I was the general dogsbody in the shop: sweeping up the old sawdust from the floor and putting new down, washing counters and so on. I didn't like that at all, so as soon as I was out on my delivery round I took as long as I possibly could at it. As this butchers made its own sausages and pies, I also had to help with that as well. So they tried to keep me busy.

I cannot remember what the wages were, I know it was not much, but I used to make quite a bit in tips on my rounds, so was not doing too badly. On pay day we were told we could have meat to take home as a perk, so this helped out indoors. Plus I used to nick quite a bit of meat, sausages and so on. The stuff I used to nick I would put into the basket that I carried my orders in, on the front of the bike, making sure that it was well hidden under the meat that I had to deliver. Some of this nicked meat I gave to my mother, the rest I used to sell to women in our street while doing my rounds. So really I was doing quite well, and was happy in my work, as I was out so long I found that I was being left out of all those odd jobs they found for me if I got back early.

I was at this job for a couple of months or so, and during that time had done nothing wrong. My main mate now was Dave, who I used to meet every night, going to the pictures or just hanging around the street corner. Dave was also working, but as a van boy on the railway.

One Saturday at work, with no orders to deliver, I was given a job to do in the basement of the shop, where normally the pies and sausages used to be made, but as they had all been done for the week, there was no one down there but me. I was supposed to be cleaning the place, but with no one to watch me I just messed about for a bit, then sat down having a smoke, idly looking around as I did so. Suddenly, I thought I saw a movement on a shelf where boxes of tickets for the meat were kept. Climbing onto a chair and shifting the box near to where I thought I had seen the movement, I got the shock of my life - a fucking great rat flew out from behind the box and hared off along the shelf, with me flat on my back on the floor, where I had fallen as soon as I had seen the rat in flight! With a yell I jumped to my feet and ran up the stairs to the shop as fast as I could, running smack into the busiest part of the day - the shop being full of women buying their Sunday joints.

As I burst through the door into the shop everything went quiet, and all eyes looked in my direction. Quiet, that is, except for me as I let out a yell, 'There's a fucking great rat down the cellar!'

With this announcement there was suddenly an uproar in the shop, a couple of the women even giving out little screams and looking down at their feet in horror. Someone shouted out, 'What's down there?'

They must have been bloody well deaf, I'd shouted out loud enough. Perhaps they were, so I shouted back to them, 'A fucking great rat!'

People began to move out of the shop which is when the manager came over to me and told me to keep quiet, and turning to the customers that were left said, 'It's alright everyone, he must be seeing things.' But I wasn't having that, and told him so. Getting hold of my arm he led me to the back room of the shop where he told me to be quiet, and went on to say, 'Don't come running into the shop saying there are rats in the cellar. You will upset all the customers.' I insisted that I had seen one, but he still tried to talk me out of it, telling me that I couldn't have done.

In the end I said, 'Sod you mate, I saw a rat and I'm going to say so! My mum gets her meat from this shop.' The fact that I was nicking the meat for her was neither here nor there, it still came out of this shop, and if it was running alive with rats, then I would tell her and her mates.

The outcome of this was that I got the sack on the spot. I stormed out of the shop with him shouting out behind me not to come back there again for anything. Well he had no fear of that. As I left the shop another queue of people were forming who had not heard about the rat, so I stood outside shouting, 'Don't go in there, there's rats in the cellar!' Some moved off, others didn't, but that was up to them. In the end out came the manager and told me that if I didn't go away, he would call the police. By now I had had my say, so left.

Without a job, it was now back to the streets and doing nothing but mooch about. My friend Dave had also got the sack from his job as a van boy on the railway, so at least I had company. Strangely enough, my brother had replaced Dave as a van boy. He told me that I could get a job there as well, but at the moment I didn't want another job as Dave and I had decided to become totters. We had seen various fellers going round the streets with barrows collecting rags and bits of old junk, calling out at the tops of their voices, 'Rags, bottles and bones!' and that seemed easy enough. Mind you, it was our intention to collect just old rags. We had already been in the bottle business and had come unstuck with the pub landlord, so didn't want anymore of that. As for bones, gawd knows what people did with them. So we would stick strictly to the rag side of things.

The problem now was to get a barrow. All the totters we spoke to hired their barrows from some firm or other on a daily basis. Dave and I having no money could not do that, but we found an old pram, so used that as a start, with the intention of hiring a barrow once we had earnt some money.

Setting out on our first day as totters we were full of confidence, which was soon to be knocked out of us. The first customer we got was a woman. She came out of her house with a big bag of old rags, but the first words she uttered made me think she was some sort of nutter as she asked, 'How much will you give me for this lot?' She must have come out of a nut house to be asking this sort of question. We told her that we were not giving money for old rags, that we were only collecting them to get them off people's hands, and that no one would give her anything for them.

But she knew different, she told us the other rag and bone men who came around gave her money. Seems like the world was full of nutters, but everywhere we went we were told the same thing.

We made one or two enquiries and found out that she and the other people we had come across that first day were right; the other totters did buy the old rags off of people, and then sold them up the rag and bone shop for a profit. So another business of ours bit the dust, but this time for lack of funds. But we kept our pram and decided to go back to nicking lead.

It was a lot harder now, but there were still one or two bomb sites about that we could raid if we were careful about it. Although we had lost touch with the bloke who used to buy our lead, we could still sell any that we got to the feller in the rag and bone shop. He even had a board outside his shop that told of the prices he would pay for different metals and so on.

Having to be extra careful about getting into the boarded-up bombed houses was a bit of a balls ache. The police were keeping a more watchful eye on them, and were forever chasing kids away, but we coped alright and were soon earning a bit of money. We went back to our old way of doing things: doing our lead-nicking by night, away from the prying eyes of the police and anyone else. Back into what we knew, we were having a lot of success gathering the lead at night and hiding it in a place that we could easily lay our hands on it the next day, then taking it up to the rag shop in our pram. The owner of the shop would put it on a large set of scales and pay the money for it, taking the money from a big wooden drawer under the shop counter. We did this for a couple of weeks or so, and were actually saving a bit of money, but that business was soon to end.

Sitting in a cafe used by all the totters, and having a bit of breakfast, we got talking to one old man who it seemed had been totting for years. He told us a tale about the rag and bone shop. It seems this old totter had caught the owner fiddling the scales, and was underpaying everyone that sold him metal. As we had been using this shop for a couple of weeks or so, Dave and I began to wonder how much he had taken us for.

Although the old totter couldn't prove it as yet, he was going to do so that very day as soon as he had finished his breakfast. Dave and I decided that we would go up there with him to see what went on. Old Bill, as the old totter was called, had already weighed a couple of sacks of rags, so knew exactly what he had. Anyway up at the rag shop he let the owner weigh the stuff up, and yes, Old Bill had less weight according to these scales than he knew he had. So then the battle of words began, Old Bill slagging the rag shop man off and telling him that he wouldn't be coming back there again, and would be telling all the totters what had been going on. There was plenty of fucking and blinding going on as Old Bill stated his case. Some words came out that I didn't even know, but all sounding quite fruity. Myself and Dave added to all of this with some of our own language, the three of us eventually walking away and going back to the cafe for another cup of tea, and reporting to all the totters that were still there what had happened.

Talking to them we asked where they were now going to sell their stuff. It seemed that they had a place over Shepherd's Bush that they could go to. Although that wasn't too far from where we lived, Dave and I didn't fancy trooping over there each day, so decided to give up totting and look around for some other way to make a living. But first of all we had some business with the rag shop man to deal with. If he was taking, or had been taking, Old Bill and the other totters on, then it was for sure he had been doing the same to us, and that we were not going to stand for at any price. We were going to rob him and knew exactly how. It was so easy I wondered why we hadn't thought of it before.

Every lunch time the owner of the shop would go to his flat above the shop for his lunch, leaving the shop empty but still open. If anyone came into the shop to do business in this period, all they had to do was pick up a hand bell that stood on the counter and ring it, and down would come the shop keeper. So it followed that anyone could walk into the shop and do as they wanted, as long as they did not ring the bell, which is what Dave and I did. Taking our old pram with us and parking it outside the shop one lunch time, taking a quick look inside to make sure he had not changed his routine, and seeing that he hadn't, into the shop we went. Dave stood by the doorway to make sure that no other customers could come in to surprise me, while I went straight behind the counter to the wooden drawer, where, as I said earlier, the owner kept his money. Having a quick look in the drawer to make sure there was money there, I was delighted to see that there was. Taking the whole drawer out of its slides, back round the counter I came, and out of the shop went Dave and I. Putting the cash drawer into our pram under some old sacks we had, off we went quite happy with our day's work so far.

Taking the money drawer back to the basement of my house, we laid a sack on the floor and up-ended the drawer to get all the coins out in one go, when, much to our surprise, the part of the drawer holding the coins fell out and underneath was a roll of ten bob notes. We were on top of the world over getting the drawer in the first place; now we were not only on top of it but out of it too. We had a count up, and we had over a hundred pounds. In those days if we had a pound we were rich, and now this. We promised each other to tell no one of how much money we had. Sharing it out we were very quiet in doing so, I think we were both a bit frightened as to how much we had. We even got rid of our old pram on a bomb site, and the drawer at the same time. There was no way that we could go splashing money about all over the place, or it would have soon got back to our mothers and they would be sure to take all the money from us. So we hid it behind a loose brick in the wall down in the basement of my house, and took just what we needed each day for fags and the pictures and so on.

With so much money we were getting itchy palms and wanted to spend more than we were doing. Then on the Saturday after having nicked the money, which was only a couple of days later, we decided to do just that. I told my mother that I wouldn't be home that night as I was going to stay with Dave, and he told his mother he was staying with me. So we were free and no one would be looking for us because we hadn't come home that night. We were off to Brighton in Sussex. We had twenty pounds each in our pockets and meant to live it up.

We bought a platform ticket instead of a train ticket and dodged on the train, as although we were rich there was no need to go throwing our money away on things that we had no need to. Our day in Brighton was to be the best in my life so far. Anything we wanted to do, we did. The piers were the highlights of our day. Fish and chips for dinner and fish and chips for tea satisfied our stomachs. There is something about Brighton that I love; being so close to Mile Oak approved school it is a wonder to me that I never hated the place. I loved the narrow winding streets off of the seafront and the smell of the sea. The atmosphere of people on holiday enjoying themselves. Something got to me inside about

Brighton. Except for telling of the everyday things about the place, I cannot describe what it is that has always attracted me to the town. I wished so much that I could spend my life there, but no, I had to go back to London. Not tonight though; the next day yes. On this day and night I wasn't going anywhere.

The evening we spent on the pier and wandering along the front, until, tired out, we made our way to a spot not far from the pier and away from the chill of the night air. Then tucking ourselves deep into our coats, fell into a deep sleep.

The following day we spent pretty much as we had the first: on the pier and just wandering about. Teatime we left Brighton to go back to London, once again dodging on the train.

Back in London life was just one big bore. Even more so, as for a while we did not have to put ourselves out to get money, having enough for our small needs. All we really needed was enough for a packet of fags and to go and sit in the local cafe all morning. We didn't even need money to go to the pictures as that was something we never paid for; it was easy to dodge in the back door. One of the good things about that was we did not have to queue. On a few occasions we would dodge into the circle of our local picture house, into the dearer seats. But we never lasted long up there, either getting slung out for causing aggro, or running out ourselves after causing a disturbance. Sitting on the front row of the circle seats we would buy a tub of icecream each, then taking the top off we would hold it upside down over the balcony. As it slowly melted and began to slide out of the tub we would take aim on someone's head below, especially if they were bald, and then wait for it to slide completely out and hurtle down onto our targets. It would land with a splosh! And then all hell was let loose from below as the first icecream bomb landed, to be followed by others. Sometimes there were as many as six or seven of us sitting in that balcony, and the icecreams would land on the heads below in rapid succession. Shouts of, 'You dirty little bastards!' would come from below, while we stood cheering from above, where those hit could not get at us. Usherettes would switch their torches on and point them in our direction, but as soon as they began to head our way, we were off out the back door and away. Usually we would then make our way to another picture house, dodge in there and settle down to watch the show. We had had our nights fun.

But I was becoming bored with being one of the idle rich, and began to hang around indoors too much, so much so that my mother kept nagging me to get a job. My brother said he thought there were jobs going where he worked, as a van boy on the railway. So I thought, why not? Dave came with me, and even though he had been sacked by the railway before, they said they would give him another chance - but if he kept being late, as he did before, it would be the sack again. I suppose because we were together, they also warned me about the same thing.

So we both started work. The driver I got was a Russian and it took me all my time to understand what the hell he was talking about. It was an easy enough job, driving from the Marylebone goods yard to other yards all over London: unload our lorry, fill it up again with stuff to take back, and so on through the day until it was time to knock off.

After a couple of days of this, the Russian began to act a bit strange. Having loaded our lorry for the first delivery, he came round to the cab where I was sitting, passed a parcel up to me, and by pointing indicated that he wanted me to hide the parcel beneath my feet. Now this was a right dodgy move but I went along with it, and would wait to see what happened. That day the first port of call was not another goods yard as it was usually, but straight round to the Russian's house. There he took the parcel from me and went into the house, coming back shortly afterwards with no parcel. From that day on, each day he would drop a parcel off at his house.

At first I took no notice of all this, but after speaking to Dave about it, and being the little thief I was, I decided that I was entitled to something out of what he was nicking, as nicking he must have been. On the very next day, having gone through the usual procedure, we pulled up outside his house and round he came from his side of the lorry to collect the parcel from me. But this time I did not pass it out, and instead said to him, 'What's your game mate?' With that he went stark raving mad, shouting and hollering at me in some gibberish. In the end, to shut him up, I passed the parcel out to him. Back on the road again we drove along in silence for a while, then he suddenly said, 'Here,' and pushed half a crown into my hand. After that, every time there was a parcel dropped off at his house (which was nearly every day) I got half a crown from him.

Then came the time I caught a heavy cold and was off work for a few days. On the day that I returned, I went to my usual spot to wait for the Russian when the yard foreman came over to me and told me I was wanted in the office, that the manager wanted to see me. Once there, I was questioned about the Russian. Had I seen him take anything from the yard? Did he drop any parcels off anywhere other than on railway property? To all these questions I answered, 'No.' I could hardly say, 'Yes,' could I? Unless I wanted to drop myself in it. I was then asked if I had taken anything out of the yard, again the answer was, 'No.' This manager must be a crackpot, I thought, surely the nutcase didn't think I was going to tell him that I had been nicking parcels with the Russian. The next question was the one though - had I ever been in trouble with the police? 'Yes,' was my answer to that. Then I was told by this manger, 'Well I'm afraid that I have to give you your cards. As you have been in trouble with the police we should not have given you a job in the first place.' Well, there was no need for him to be afraid about it as I didn't give a shit whether he sacked me or not.

As soon as Dave heard that I had been sacked, he gave the job up too. So for the both of us it was back to the streets to earn our living. Several times I went round to the Russian's house and knocked on his door but never got an answer, even though a couple of times I'm sure that someone was in, as I saw the curtains move. I even shouted through the letter box a few times, but after a few days of getting blanks I gave up. I was never to see that Russian again, even though I passed his house many a time and always looked. The curtains were always drawn, and the house had a dead look about it.

But back to the routine of doing nothing and spending money faster than I liked, and now more so as I wasn't earning any from anywhere else. On top of that, Dave and I had picked up a couple of tarts one night at the pictures, so we had them to take out and spend money on, which was a bit of a balls ache. We did suggest to them one night, as we were heading for a night up the local Odeon cinema, that the four of us should go around to the back door and dodge in, but they said no to that. So we suggested that, ok, if they didn't want to dodge in, that Dave and I would pay for them to go in, and once in, one of them could go to the back door and open it for us. At least that would save us a couple of bob. But they got all up in the air about that and said that they were not used to this type of thing, and they thought we were decent boys, and if they knew we were like this they would not have come out with us in the first place. Well, Dave and I were not used to this bollocks either and told them so, and backed it up by telling them that we weren't used to paying for two tarts to go to the pictures every night, and what's more, we were not used to tarts that could be picked up so easily in the pictures, so could piss off as quick as they liked! Now they told us that they would tell their dads what we had said to them. There was only one answer to that, and that was, 'Bollocks to your dads!' That was what they were told, and off they went with their noses in the air.

Dave and I waited outside the back door of the pictures, and as soon as someone came out, we held the door open and in we went to see the film, and what's more enjoyed it. All the more without those soppy tarts who wanted to hold hands, and old cobblers like that. Why we ever got lumbered up with them in the first place, I don't know.

three old birds

I HAD STARTED THE THIRD YEAR OF MY TEENS and was going nowhere. I was leading a pretty aimless sort of life, just going along with the flow of things. I had no ambitions at all. If I was getting around the streets and had a few bob in my pockets, then that was plenty for me. I was getting nagged at home about getting a job, so much so that in the end I pretended I had one. Now I had to leave the house in the morning and not come back until teatime, pretending to be at work. This didn't bother me as I was usually out of the house all day anyway, and at times not even bothering to come home until late at night, and then straight to bed. Making out to be going to work caused a problem though; if I was in work I was expected to give my mother some of my wages towards my keep. So I now had to make the money for that. I also had to buy some wage packets and make them up each week. I would never pass the wage packet to my mother, just open it in front of her, give the couple of bob she asked for, and that was that. Sometimes, if I had not had a good week, I had barely enough in the packet to pay her what she wanted. So there I was, stuck with the problem of finding or nicking enough money each week to pay my mother. At times I felt it would be a lot easier to get a job, but that thought did not stay with me too long. Dave had also told his mother the same thing that I had, so at least I had someone with me with the same problem.

We found one fairly easy way to nick money, to start off with at least, and that was off of buses. Conductors had the habit of making a count of the money they had collected and bagging it up, and then putting the bagged-up money into a small attaché case which in turn they put into a cupboard under the bus stairway, a cupboard they did not lock. At the end of every bus route there was a cafe or coffee stall of some sort into which the driver and conductor would go for a snack, leaving the bus unattended. So it was a matter of seconds for either Dave or myself to get on the bus, nick the attaché case with the money in it, while the other one would keep watch, and off we would go to have a share-out. But as time went by, conductors became less trusting in leaving their boxes on the buses when they went for their break, and would take the attaché cases into the cafe or to the coffee stall with them.

Now we actually started to board buses and go for rides to the ends of the routes. While on the buses we would keep an eye on the conductor, and as he made the money up as the bus went along, we would weigh up how much we thought was now in the case. Once we had the idea there was enough for our needs, we would wait for the conductor to go upstairs to collect fares. Then waiting for the bus to slow down or stop at traffic lights, we would grab the attaché case, jump off the bus and away! But this was a hit and miss affair. Waiting for all these things to coincide before we were able to nick the money was a bit too much at times. On other occasions we never actually saw the conductor put any money in the attaché case, but assumed he must have done so before we got on, so we would nick the case only to find on opening it that it was empty.

Even the mode of nicking off of buses was coming to an end, so Dave and I sacked ourselves from our pretend jobs. My mother wasn't too pleased about that, but at least it relieved the pressure from me having to find money for wages each week, and the same for Dave. From that moment my mother also stopped nagging me about getting work. I feel she was gradually giving up with me.

Back once again to just mooching round the streets, staying out until all hours of the night, and sleeping late in the mornings. This in itself was a bit of a job, as my bedroom being also the kitchen-come-sitting room I had to get up while everyone else got ready for work, and once my mother was up everyone had to be up. It was just a matter of waiting for her to leave the house, and then go back to bed for a couple of hours, at times not even to sleep but just lie there in a stupor until it was time to get up and go and meet Dave. Things were going from bad to worse. Money was, or seemed to be, hard to get hold of. We tried a couple of our old schemes like totting, but with no success. So it was time to sit down and really rethink our lives, but nothing was coming to mind too quickly as we discussed ways of making money. We even talked of robbing a bank. How the hell we were going to do that I don't know! We tried shoplifting, but after a couple of attempts at that, which were complete failures, we gave that up as we didn't fancy people chasing us down the street shouting, 'Stop thief!' as they had once. What could we do? Of course we could have got a job, but what good was that? We would only get the sack, we had even had to sack ourselves one time! This was really becoming a problem. In the end we came to a decision - we would become burglars.

Once we had decided to become burglars, the problems began. How to go about it? Where were we to get our burglar's tools from? We could hardly go to our mums and ask them for the money to buy the equipment. We had seen burglars at the pictures, and they always seemed to have a bag of tools with them. Now the first thing we had to do before setting out on this new business was to nick some tools. In the end it wasn't too much of a problem. Both Dave and I got enough tools to start us up from our homes, tools of every description. In fact we finished up with so many tools we had to store some in the basement of my house. We had an old plumber's bag that I had found indoors, and into that we put screwdrivers, a couple of hammers, pliers and so on. Now we were set, ready to become fully-fledged burglars.

We chose a block of mansions close to where we lived as our first target. Dressed in our darkest clothes we headed for the mansions. It was broad daylight, so why we picked dark clothes to wear I don't know, unless again we were following the burglars from the films we had seen, as they all appeared to dress in black. Taking turns to carry the heavy bag of tools we soon reached the block of mansions. Getting into the block itself caused no problem, we simply walked straight in through the front door. But as we made our way to the stairway leading to the upper floors, I was suddenly rooted to the spot by a voice calling out, 'Hello Ron, what are you up to?'

Turning quickly round to face this voice, I saw standing before me a neighbour of mine. The only thing I could think to say to him was, 'Charlie, what are you doing here?' It seemed he worked in these mansions as a porter, and there he stood in his gold braid uniform, looking like one of the Yankee officers I had seen in the war. Now of course he wanted to be nosey, and wanted to know what Dave and I had in our bag. But we ignored that, and him too, and made our way back to the front door. Charlie just stood there grinning, and just as we reached the front door he called out, 'Yes you had better go Ron. I will let your mum know that I saw you today.' It looked as if this burglary game wasn't going to be as easy as it looked, or rather that we thought it would be.

Of course Charlie did tell my mother he had seen Dave and me.

When she asked me what I was up to round there, I told her we were totting. All she said to that was, 'People do not go totting round that way. So be careful.' Now we really had to weigh up the situation, we had to have a rethink. We did, and decided that it would be a lot better to go round 'casing the places' first, another expression we had heard on films, and far better too to go to an area where it was unlikely we would bump into someone we knew. So, leaving our tools stashed in my cellar, we set off for areas new.

Our first choice, in fact, was only half a mile from where we lived, so we were not too far afield. This area, St. John's Wood, was a rich area, the houses and flats really upper class, and as burglars it suited our purpose. On our first day looking around this area all we did was to dodge in and out of buildings, saying to each other, 'This looks good. We can get into one of these flats,' or houses, whichever we were casing at the time.

After about an hour of this ducking and diving, we gave up our hunt for the day. Not by choice, but because we got stopped by the police. It seemed that someone had phoned them saying that there were two suspicious characters in the area, unbeknown to us of course! Coming out of a block of flats, there at the kerbside a police car was parked. Trying not to act the least bit suspicious, we walked past the car in which two coppers were sitting, but having barely put a foot past it, a voice called out, 'You two stay just where you are.' There was no point running and, as we had so far done nothing, we did as we were told.

One of the coppers got out of the car and headed in our direction. As he did so he asked us, 'What do you two think you're up to?'

'Nothing,' we both said together.

Back came another question, 'If you're up to nothing, why are you walking in and out of flats?'

'Just looking,' we told him.

'Looking for what?' he asked. Well there was no anwser to that, so we both kept quiet.

Having sat in the police car until now, the second copper decided to get out and join in. Now what the hell was going on? This second copper we knew. He was none other than the one who used to walk the beat round the streets where we lived. The same one who had given us warnings when we had followed the woman spy, and had beaten up her kid. Now he stood before us and just stared. Eventually he spoke, which pleased me as he was beginning to unnerve me as he had a piercing sort of stare. It was as though he was looking right through us. He never used to have that look, and I did wonder where he had picked up that habit. Perhaps it was something they taught in the police force. Anyway his words to us were, 'You two are up to no good. Now get off of these streets and back to where you live. If we find you roaming around these streets again, you're nicked! Understand?' Of course we understood, did he think we were thick or something? But we didn't put that to him, we just got out of it a bit quick.

We were both a bit pissed off with this burglary lark. It seemed everywhere we went, someone knew us. So we had to look for another way to make a living, and at some place where people would not keep asking who we were, or what we were up to. We had to have a serious chat about this carry on, so we arranged to meet the following day at Smokey Joe's, our favourite cafe. We then split up and retired for the day.

The next day, in the cafe, we came to the conclusion that as yet we were not cut out to be burglars, and would have to find some other way to make a living. Once again someone suggested that we get a job, and once again we ignored the advice. It was too good wandering the streets as we had done throughout the war, free to come and go as we pleased. We went back to a bit of shoplifting and were doing quite well, but of course we knew this was a risky business, and so it proved to be, and, for me, very costly.

Strolling along the Edgware Road one afternoon, looking for something to nick, we passed a newsagents. Glancing in, we noticed a carton of cigarettes just sitting on the floor on the customer side of the counter, just offering itself up to be stolen. Strolling casually into the shop, making sure to leave the door open for a quick getaway, we both made a grab for the carton of fags, bumped into each other and both ended up draped over the carton. Suddenly there was uproar. A shout went up, 'What do you think you're up to?' Ignoring this question we both regained our feet. Dave now had a firm hold on the carton of fags and took to his heels out of the shop with them, closely followed by me, and the pair of us just as closely followed by the shop owner, as it was him doing all the shouting. Even with his burden Dave had a head start on me, and was round a corner and out of sight when the ton of bricks hit me, knocking me to the pavement with a thud. On top of me was the shopkeeper.

Well, the police were called and I was nicked. Everyone had the hump with me because I would not tell them who was with me; none more so than the three old ladies that I now had to appear before again, at the same juvenile court that I had been to on a couple of previous occasions.

So back to the same court, sitting in the same chair, as was my mother behind me. In front of me, the same women. Didn't they ever have a day off? The case was put after I had pleaded guilty, the copper giving all the gory details; telling of how I would not give the police any assistance, that I would not name the other person with me, and so on. The old bird in the centre of the three did not once look in the direction of the copper as he was giving his evidence. All she did was to sit staring at me. If she had been younger and in a different situation, I would have wondered if she fancied me or something.

Once the copper had finished his bit, only then did she look away, and spoke to the copper saying, 'Is there anything known about this boy?' There had to be something wrong with her eyesight. I had been in front of her a couple of times, and here she was asking a question as though I was a stranger to her. Anyway, the copper soon put her wise to who I was and what I had done in the past.

After all that palavar was over and done with, she then looked back at me again and said, 'You are turning into a thug. You have been up in front of this court before. We even sent you to an approved school, from which we hoped you would benefit, but obviously not. You will now go to a senior approved school, where hopefully you will learn to become a better citizen. Take him away.'

That is an expression that I have heard many times over the years. It seemed to me as time went by that judges, magistrates and anyone having anything to do with the law must have learnt this expression, 'Take him away', at whatever school they went to. But all that is neither here nor there at this moment in time.

escape from Eye

HAVING BEEN SENT TO A SENIOR APPROVED SCHOOL, I got the usual tears from my mother, and once again was told to be a good boy. There was no chance of that though. As soon as I could, I would be off and running. This time I did not have to wait for too long in the remand home at the back of the court, just a couple of hours. I was taken straight to this approved school, which was in Eye, Suffolk. On arriving there, I found the procedure no different to that of Mile Oak: in front of the headmaster, listening to his drivel about how easy it was to escape, but I would be caught and severely punished when I was. The system of dormitories was the same except that here there was no fancy names, just numbers. I was to become used to this in the coming years.

There was no initiating ceremony. I expect we were all too big or too old for that sort of stuff. What there was was a lot of eyeing up and weighing up of the new boy. I took no notice of this as I wasn't going to be there long enough to become involved in any old bollocks.

The first day, or what was left of it, I kept pretty much to myself as I did not want anyone to get a hint of what I was going to do. Come bedtime it was the same rigmarole as at Mile Oak: lights on for a while, then when the lights were put out, no talking. I waited patiently for the lights to be put out, and not giving the master who had done the turning out more than a couple of minutes, I got up and began to dress. Questions were being thrown at me as to what I was doing. There was even a dormitory captain who wanted to make himself busy, telling me that I couldn't run off as I would get the rest of the dorm into trouble. How he worked that out I don't know, but was to find out later. If any boy ran off in the night, then those left in his dorm were punished by being given extra duties, for not informing on him.

Anyway, this dorm captain looked as if he was going to get out of bed and perhaps try to do something to stop me. I went right up to him and said, 'You mind your own fucking business what I'm going to do!' then walked away from him. Looking back as I got to the dorm door, I was pleased to see he had gone back to bed.

This time there was no fire escape to walk down. It was just a matter of walking straight down the communal stairway and out of the front door, hoping that I would not bump into any of the masters, which happily I did not. Once out of the school grounds it was just a matter of running as fast as I could to put as much distance between myself and the school before there was a check, and, still not being sure of this dorm captain, before he could report me. So I made a fast retreat. I kept to the roads for a mile or so, but soon got fed up with jumping in and out of hedges every time a car's headlights approached, as to me every car was a police car. So I took to the fields, or attempted to do so.

Still walking in the road until I spotted a gap in the hedge, strolling casually over to it quite unconcerned, and then came the shock - the ground opened up beneath my feet, and I found myself in four foot of water that froze the balls off of me! I'd walked right into an overgrown ditch. Feeling really pissed off with this, I didn't give a shit if I got caught or not. What the hell was I doing in the middle of nowhere when I could be in a nice warm bed? I even began to think that perhaps this approved school wasn't such a bad place, and that I should settle down!

I quickly got out of the ditch, and after this mishap kept strictly to the roads, hoping for a police car to come along, but it wasn't to be. I seemed to walk for miles, passing through villages where I suppose I could have given myself up. The fact is I didn't, I trudged on. Then as if I didn't have enough to contend with, the heavens opened and it started to piss down with rain! It came down in buckets, but through it I walked. Now I wasn't the least bit depressed, I just wished to fuck I was dead!

After what seemed like hours, some way ahead I noticed a kind of glow in the sky, perhaps this was heaven and my wish had been granted. But no it hadn't, the glow ahead was the town of Ipswich. Walking through the streets shortly after, I was getting some peculiar stares, which is not surprising as other than me everyone had umbrellas up and macintoshes on, while I was walking along like a drowned rat. People seemed to be giving me a wide berth and who could blame them, covered in dirt as I was from the ditch, and saturated with rain water, I must have looked like an escaped lunatic. But I ignored them as much as they did me, as having reached this town my spirits had perked up. This being a big town there had to be a railway station, but where? I just had to ask someone.

The next person that I came across I stopped, and said, 'Excuse me mate, can you tell me where the train station is?'

The answer I got from him was a bit of a surprise. 'It's not the train station you want son, it's the police station. You're from Kerrison Approved School, and you had better come along with me!'

So there I was, nicked again! Of all the people to stop, I had to pick on an off-duty CID man from the local nick. But for once I didn't really worry too much about getting nicked, it was a pleasure to get into the warmth of the police station, being so cold, wet and hungry. The warmth of the place was pure luxury. I was taken to a wash room and told to have a shower, and then wrap a couple of towels around myself. After having done that I sat in front of a coal fire, was given a cup of cocoa, and told not to move. Move, the whole bloody police force couldn't move me! I've loved cocoa ever since that night.

Later I was collected by one of the masters from the school, the journey back taking a bloody sight less time than it took me. It seemed I had hardly sat in the car than I was back at the school. Back to the same old shit of being taken to the headmaster's office, given a lecture by him on the error of my ways, and then he walked away from me to a cupboard. From that he took a cane, a replica to the one that Olive Oil used back at Mile Oak. But this headmaster had a problem as I was not a replica of that boy that stood for caning anymore. I was older and bigger, and not in the least bit frightened of this master. Of course I had to go through the motions of letting him tell me to hold my hand out ready for caning. But no sooner had he said the words, he got a reply from me, and one that seemed to take his breath away. 'Fuck you!' I told him. 'You or no one else is ever going to hit me with one of those fucking things again!'

Then the strangest thing happened. I was all set to fight him if needs be, but he walked up to me, looked right at me and said, 'Go to your dorm and tell no one of what has happened here.'

Going to the dorm I felt so uptight and not in the mood to be fucked about by anyone at all, but I was going to be. As soon as I got in the dorm, the dorm captain got out of bed and came up to me and said, 'I knew you would get caught.' Then, grinning all over his face, he went to walk away from me. It was then that I smacked him full on the nose. All hell broke loose then as a couple of his mates jumped me, and punches were coming from every angle. Help was at hand though as two other boys jumped in on my side, which was a bit of a surprise. The noise that was being kicked up soon brought masters running. Once they were in the room, this dorm captain showed his true colours. He began to shout, pointing at me, 'He started it!' I was taken out of the dorm and put into what they called the 'secure room' for the night, which caused me no concern. As soon as my head hit the pillow I was asleep.

The following morning it was back to the headmaster's office. This time there was no threat of the cane, just a lot of shouting: you're nothing but a thug, that I would end up in trouble all my life unless I conformed. Those words meant nothing to me at the time, but how very true they were to become. I was released from the secure room, and put straight back into the same dorm, when I fully expected to be put into a different one. Once back in the dorm it soon became clear why; the dorm captain had been moved out to the only other dormitory there was, so peace reigned.

For the next few days I drifted along with the way things were run, so much so that the headmaster approached me and said, 'I'm pleased to see that you have settled down.' I didn't even bother to answer him as I knew that as soon as I was ready I would be off again. Ready I was within a couple of days, when I was approached by the couple of boys who had helped me against the dorm captain and his mates. It seemed that as they knew I had been caught in Ipswich, they thought that I knew the way. I had to put them straight about that! I knew the direction but not the way. They were satisfied with that, and the sooner we were off the better, the three of us decided.

Both these boys had been at Kerrison for a few months, and they knew the full layout; what was the best time to go and so on. They also knew where there was some money kept in the headmaster's office, which would be a big help. In the school there was also a bike shed, of which I knew nothing. We made our plans to go on the weekend when there were not so many masters on duty. The next Saturday was to be the day, as we found out that the headmaster would be away for the whole of the weekend, and indeed until the Monday, which was just fine as we could steal the money. It would not be missed until he got back.

Came the Saturday, John, the boy who knew where the money

was kept, said it would be far better if he went and got it himself rather than the three of us wandering about, and getting in each other's way. So Lee, the other boy, and myself stayed in the dorm, waiting to see the outcome, which turned out better than expected. Besides finding about forty pounds in notes and coins, he also came back with about twenty post office savings books belonging to some of the boys at the school. And what particularly pleased me, one of them belonged to our ex-dorm captain. These books were as good as money, as they were the savings stamp sort that could be changed at any post office. Now that that part of our plan had been successful, we were full of hope for the rest of it. We just had to wait now for the right time of night to come so that we could carry our plans out in full.

We waited until about eleven o'clock. Once again it was just a matter of making our way carefully down the stairs, and out the front door of the school, which was done easily enough. Once out in the grounds we made our way to the bike shed. There was no need to break in. The door, it seemed, was always unlocked. In the bike shed we closed the door behind us, Lee lit the torch that he had with him, and began to look at the bikes, making sure that we did not take one that had a puncture or something wrong with it. Suddenly there was a voice at the door shouting, 'Come out, I know you're in there!' To say there was panic stations is to put it mildly, all three of us trying to get out of a small window at the back of the bike shed at the same time!

In the end we calmed down, even though the voice was still calling for us to come out. It seemed obvious that whoever was shouting had no intention of coming in, for the present at least. Now we were settled, John got through the window followed by me. We stood waiting for Lee to get out. His head had barely appeared at the window, when he let out a yell, 'Some bastard's got my legs!' Whoever had been out there had now screwed up the courage to go into the shed. There was a shout from whoever it was, 'Come back you little sod!' Whoever it was had hold of Lee's feet had to be blind to call that out, as at sixteen Lee was six feet tall in his socks. A tug of war began with Lee as the rope; John and I pulling him one way, and whoever the other way. John and I won, as with one desperate pull Lee came out of that window like greased lightning, with the three of us collapsing in a heap behind the bike shed. Hearing footsteps from round the side of the shed, we quickly regained our feet and took off out of it, a bit lively. There was a lot of shouting from behind but no one followed us. We were free.

After running a couple of miles we slowed down, and climbed a fence into a field, where we sat for a while to rest and consider our next move. Unfortunately Lee had lost his shoes to whoever had been hanging onto him. He had also torn the arse out of his trousers, so he was none too pleased with life. We decided to stick to the fields, at least for a while, as it was certain that we had been reported missing. So, except for Lee who had a cold arse and sore feet, we were quite content.

We walked for hours, or so it seemed, in the direction I knew Ipswich to be. After a few miles we came across a barn which we went into for a bit more rest. Once rested, we again set off, but within a matter of minutes we came across a farm, in the yard of which stood a milk tanker. Now for some reason Lee told us that he could drive, which was handy as now we could nick the tanker and make the rest of our escape in comfort. Checking all the buildings to make sure that there was no one around, we climbed into the tanker, with Lee behind the steering wheel. The tanker was a self starter, so, with a roar loud enough to wake the dead, Lee started up, with John and myself looking anxiously out of the windows to see if we had disturbed anyone. All appeared well, that is until we began to move. With Lee having put his foot on the accelerator, we sped out of that farm yard at two hundred miles an hour, and at the same speed hit the hedge on the other side of the road, where the engine died on us. We picked ourselves up from the floor of the driving cab, and departed from the tanker faster than it had crossed the road.

So it was back to the fields. By now though we were knackered, so decided to have a bit of a kip under a hedge. We must have slept the 'sleep of the just' as when we awoke it was daylight, and in the field in front of us a man was at work. We sat there in silence for a while watching him. It was a warm pleasant morning so we were quite content. Suddenly John piped up, 'His coat is hanging up in the hedge over there!' Now with the arse hanging out of his trousers, Lee decided that the man's coat was for him. So, Indian fashion, he crawled round the hedges to nick the coat, while John and I sat back to watch, ready to leap to our feet and run if anything went wrong. Lee suddenly disappeared from sight. The coat seemed to take on a life of its own, and vanished through the hedgegrow. Then a hand appeared from the bottom of the hedge and began to snake its way along the ground. What the hell Lee thought he was up to, heaven alone knew! Eventually he got back to us. Besides the coat, with a lunch box full of delicious sandwiches.

We didn't stop to eat the sandwiches there, but made our way as quickly as we could away from that field, and not until several fields separated us from that farm worker did we stop to dine. I hadn't felt the least bit hungry until those delicious ham and cheese sandwiches came to light. With the lovely crusty bread they were made with, I can honestly say I have never tasted food like that again.

After having eaten we were on our way once more, only this time determined not to stop until we reached Ipswich. We reached the town much quicker than we thought we would. The next problem was to find a shoe shop as Lee was now bare footed, having thrown his socks away. They had worn through with all the walking we had done, and his feet were now bleeding. But of course, it was now Sunday, and there seemed little hope of finding a shop open that sold shoes. Wandering through the town, all the while keeping a careful eye out for any coppers, we came across a second-hand shop that was open. With little hope we looked in the window to see if there were any old shoes for sale. The only thing we could see in that line was a pair of old football boots, and the biggest pair that I had ever seen in my life. They must have previously belonged to a giant. There was nothing left to do but go in and buy the boots. Lee protested, but only half-heartedly, as by now his feet were really sore and bleeding. Having bought the boots, we went and sat in a bus shelter and pulled out the studs. Lee was now flat footed in football boots, and boots that were several sizes too big for him, even though he had big feet of his own, taking a pair of size ten.

As we strolled through the town, Lee was getting angrier and angrier. People we passed were grinning at him. God knows what they thought he was up to in those boots, not knowing what we did. Even John and I were laughing at him. In the end he had to laugh himself, which was a relief as a couple of times he wanted to have a go at some of the people who laughed at him, and we couldn't afford that to happen. In the end we found a cafe that was open, so settled down in there with our feet under the table. At least John and I did, while Lee had his feet under our table, and the next one to it.

We sat in that cafe for as long as we could, then spent the rest of the morning, and the early part of the afternoon, in the park. The afternoon, or the latter part of it, we spent in the pictures. The film we saw, I can still clearly recall, was 'The Adventures of Tom Sawyer'. Leaving the cinema we asked one of the usherettes where the station was; it being safer to do that than risk asking someone in the street as I had done before. Getting the whereabouts of the station from her, that was where we headed as soon as we left the cinema. Once at the station we decided to dodge the train, in spite of the fact we had money. Why break the habit of a lifetime? We struck lucky too, having no problem in getting onto the platform where the London train was aready waiting.

Boarding the train we hid ourselves in the toilet until the train pulled away from the station. We then made ourselves comfortable in an empty carriage. Nothing went wrong for us on the journey, nor did it when we arrived in London. All the ticket collectors must have been on strike, not that we were complaining. The only problem we had was caused indirectly by Lee. As we passed a group of girls on the way out of the station they began to giggle and one of them shouted out, 'Oi, kipper feet!'

At this Lee had had enough, and wanted to go over and give her a clump, so we had to hold him back. But on the way past them he called back to the girl, 'How's your tits?' which set the girls off laughing again.

The main thing was we were now in London, but we now had the problem of what we were going to do. I lived in west London, while John and Lee lived in east London at West Ham, but we did not want to split up. In the end we decided that we would go round to my mother's to see if we could stop there for the night, and then perhaps we could go and see John and Lee's families the following day. But that was not to happen. We did go to my mother's only to find that the police had been looking for me, and had also asked about the other two. Evidently the police had told my mother that they would be back. My mother gave us something to eat and drink. Of course she wanted me to give myself up, but once she saw that I was determined not to she gave up on the idea. My mother then came up with an idea that was to help us.

A friend of hers had gone into hospital, and having lived on her own for years and with no family, she had left the keys to her flat with my mother so that my mother could keep an eye on things for her. My mother suggested that we stay there, which suited us, and gave me the keys. I knew where her friend lived, in fact it was at the far end of the same street in which my mother lived, so we had to be careful with the local police who knew me. My mother gave us strict instructions to keep the place clean and tidy, and not to break anything. If we looked after the place we could possibly stay there for a few weeks as her friend looked like being in hospital for a while. Now the three of us had somewhere to stay together; neither John or Lee wanted to go over to their homes.

There was something strange about being given the keys to a flat where we could live on our own, with no parents, teachers or approved school masters. It gave me a sense of being able to do as I liked. Where my childhood had gone I didn't really know, nor at the time did I care. It just seemed to me that I had spent my life so far under other people's control, at times a control that was brutal. Now I had a flat of my own, already it was mine, I didn't consider the woman in hospital whose flat it was. It was mine to come and go as I pleased. I was just over fifteen now, in years still young, but in mind an adult. In fact I'd felt like an adult for some time now, while at the same time detesting most of the adults I had been in close contact with.

So the three of us spent our first night in London in the comfort of a flat, and without a care in the world. We did not wake until midday, and, although there was every facility in the flat, there was no food, so I introduced John and Lee to Smokey Joe's cafe, where the three of us had a large breakfast. We met friends of mine in there. It seemed everyone knew that we were on the run, and that the police were looking for us. We were gangsters! In the ensuing weeks we acted like thugs, but all that was to come.

We had the money that we had stolen from the approved school, plus the post office savings books. With these, we spent most of our first afternoon going into post offices and converting them into cash. That night we headed for the bright lights of the West End. Even though I had lived close to the West End most of my life, I had never been there at night. The darkness of the night was taken away by the flashing lights of the advertising. The crowds, and the amusement arcades, we stared at with excitement in our eyes and hearts. This was the life for us! Here was the excitement, with the hordes of people thronging the streets, all of them laughing as though they did not have a care in the world. Couples walked by arm in arm, stopping here and there to kiss, which now to me did not seem so soppy. I wanted to be part of this as did John and Lee, and for a few weeks we were.

That first night we spent in the West End until the early hours of the morning. We gorged ourselves on hot chestnuts bought from a man on a stall that had an open fire, hot dogs and ice cream, going back to our flat to sleep the sleep of the dead, but full of contentment. Each night we went back to the West End, it was like a drug to us. But gradually we were running out of money, so we had to make a plan as to how we were going to get more. We didn't want to lose the image we had of ourselves as bigshots, or to lose the way of life that we had now found in the West End. The only way I knew to get money was to nick it, or to nick something that could be sold. John and Lee were of a like mind, so we set off on a crime spree.

gangsters

OUR MAIN SOURCE OF INCOME was to be from burglary. Mostly we would go out at night to see what we could nick. Burglarly was far easier than I thought it to be when I tried it with my old mate Dave, who incidently had moved away from the old area and with whom I had now lost contact. John and Lee had dabbled in burglary before, which was why they were at Kerrison Approved School. Although they had not been nicked together, and in spite of the fact that they came from the same area, they did not know each other until they met at Kerrison. The reason for going out to do a burglary at night was quite simply because in the dark it was easier to see if people were in or out, the lights of their houses indicating that to us. Entry to houses was easy; it just meant walking into the back garden of a darkened house, putting a coat or some such thing up against a window to deaden the sound, give it a whack with a brick and we were in. We managed to get into several houses in this way in the St. John's Wood area, which pleased me after my abortive attempt with Dave. Once in these houses we would grab anything we thought was sellable, like radios, clocks and so on. For some reason or other it never entered our heads to go upstairs in these houses, being satisfied with taking all we could carry from the ground floors.

All the stuff that we nicked from the houses I sold to an uncle of mine. He was a bit of a thief himself. At the time I did not know exactly what his game was, but he always seemed to be in trouble, the same as I was. Police were always looking for him for some reason or other. He was my uncle from my mother's side of the family, being her youngest brother. He would give us a few pounds for what we had nicked, on the same night that we nicked it. As soon as he had paid us we were away up to the West End, but of course the following day we would be skint once again. It was an expensive game going to amusement arcades, the pictures and eating hot dogs up West.

One night after selling my uncle our collection of radios, clocks and such like he sat down and had a good talk to us, which amounted to him giving us a bit of training or advice. He asked us why we never seemed to get any jewellery or silver, asking us if we ever went into the bedrooms in the houses we broke into. Of course we had to tell him no, and that we only grabbed what we could from downstairs, thinking that what we took was about the only things we would be able to sell. He soon put us wise about that, telling us that he would give us more money for jewellery and silver than he was giving us for all the other stuff we were nicking. After this talk, on our next venture we forgot about the downstairs and made our way straight to the upper floors and the bedrooms. Yes, we found the jewellery, a box of it: rings, watches, necklaces and bracelets. All sparkling gold and glass of different colours. We also found about three hundred pounds in notes, so we were made. My uncle bought the jewellery for fifteen pounds. Now we had over a hundred pounds each so we were off up West to have a good time.

We got up there about ten o'clock which we found was about the best time, when the crowds were at their largest. We did the usual thing of eating and going into the arcades, but tonight there was a difference. I was drunk. We had been into an off-licence and bought some cans of beer and had sat under Eros drinking some of them. My head was really spinning. The lights of the advertising seemed to be flashing faster and looking a lot brighter than ever before. After sitting under Eros for a while, off we set for another walk about, swigging our cans of booze. At one stage I was a step or two behind the others when suddenly a woman stepped out from a doorway, and came to stand in front of me. She then asked me, 'Are you looking for a good time?' Now this soppy prat had to be one of the cranks I had heard about who frequented the West End, as what the fuck did she think I was doing? I was thoroughly enjoying myself! Later I was to find out that she was not a nutter, and exactly what she was talking about.

Lyons Corner House in Coventry Street was the best hang-out of all, as it was open all night, and was full of flashly-dressed men, who were obviously gangsters, and the women with them, their molls. The men always seemed to have their heads together whispering to each other, while the women were talking rather loudly and screeching at each other. As we sat there watching this I thought that I would like to be a part of all this. Years later I was to be, only to find that it was not what I'd thought as a fifteen year old.

On this night we left the Corner House to have a final walk around before going home. As we strolled around the streets I was approached by another woman who wanted to know if I wanted to have a good time. While in the Corner House we had talked about these woman asking this sort of thing, and John appeared to know more about it than Lee or I. He told us these women wanted to be fucked. Well, although I had not fucked any woman so far, I had a good idea of what it meant. The three of us had agreed that the next time one of us was approached we would have this good time. So this time I said yes, I wanted a good time.

Now this woman told me it was two pounds for a knee trembler or a fiver to go to her home. Well, as my knees were already trembling I said I'd have a fiver's worth, but even then only after consultation with the other two, and telling them that the woman wanted paying for a fuck. At first we were inclined to tell her to piss off, but decided the hell with it! We had money and if that is what they did in the West End then let's get on with it! After all, didn't the thirteen year old back in the war days want sweets to let us all in our camp have a look? At least this time we were going further than that, but this woman wouldn't take a fiver off of each of us, just one which happened to be me, the first one she spoke to. She called some friends of hers over, and the other two were soon fitted up with women, telling each other we would meet back at the flat later.

I didn't have to go far with the woman that I was with as her place was just at the back of Piccadilly. Home for her was just one room, and all there was in there was a large double bed and a couple of chairs. Once in the room the woman asked for five pound, which I gave her. She then started to take her clothes off while I watched. As soon as she had finished undressing, she lay down on the bed, then looking up at me she said, 'Well aren't you going to get undressed too?' Rather hesitantly I did, and got on the bed with her. I won't go into what went on, but it was as good as anything I'd had before, and I was determined to have some more of the same, which I did over the next couple of weeks or so.

The only thing I will say is that the woman earnt her money as she showed me exactly what I had to do, and a lot more besides, especially when she found out I was just over fifteen. I call her a woman, but in actual fact she was not a lot older than I was as I was to find out, as I had a good time with her on quite a few occasions after that first time. She was eighteen, in fact I got quite fond of her, and even had a few freebies with her when she had finished her work. Even on the nights that I did not go with her, we always stopped and spoke if we saw each other. To me that girl, for that is what she was, was one of the nicest women that I met. She was totally honest in what she was doing, and I was to find out in years to come that she was loyal. Even though she did what she did to earn a living, she was loyal to her boyfriend. In later years when I was to meet her again, her boyfriend of then was in prison, and as much as some of the fellers who hung around the West End tried to pull her she stayed loyal to her feller in the nick. Except for the business side of things. I know that her feller tried to get her off of the game. As it was he was a good thief, and used to earn quite a bit of money, but she wouldn't have that.

But back to John, Lee and myself. Money didn't seem to mean much to us except as a means to an end, the ends and means being exactly what we wanted to do. Between burglary and trips to the West End our nights were well catered for. Our days were spent sleeping until three or four in the afternoon. Some of the three hundred pounds we had nicked we spent on clothes. We bought a suit each, and all the rest of the gear to go with them: shirt, tie and shoes. We really did ourselves up. Once we had all this gear on we could strut about, and feel the part that we wanted to feel, bigshots. We were suited and booted, and we had money in our pockets. We could sit in the Lyons Corner House with the best of them. We could even put our heads together like they did. The fact that we never had a clue to what all the others were whispering about, and we just whispered a lot of old bollocks to each other, was neither here nor there. The only thing is we did not have a lot of women hanging round us like the other fellers did. Only on the one night did we have that.

One evening we were sitting at our usual table in the Corner House - everyone else seemed to have their own table each night, so why not us? - when the woman I had been to bed with a few times came into the place, and seeing me came over to our table, plonked her arse down on the spare chair, and sat talking to us for a while. I went to the tea counter and bought her a cup of tea, and did I strut and pose that night! Even the fact that she only sat with us a short while couldn't take the feeling away; that because she had done so, we were now truly part of the West End scene.

As the nights and weeks went by we were getting nods from other people in the Corner House. Although they never spoke to us, they nodded and gave tight-lipped smiles, which we gave back. Now that we were part of the scene up West, we were as good as any of them. Hadn't we been with some of the women that they sat with? And behind their backs we gave broad smiles, and winks to those women we had been with. What's more, some of the women winked back. All great stuff!

This burglary game that we were in seemed to be a full-time job in the early part of the evenings. Quite a few times we were seen, and on a couple of occasions were chased from someone's house when they took us by surprise by coming in on us. And now things were becoming very dodgy, the police were calling at my mother's regularly looking for us. They had even told my mother that they wanted to see the three of us about burglaries. We were being seen far too often in areas where quite a few burglaries had taken place, and had been chased too many times. Now we couldn't venture out of our flat during the day as we could hardly wander around the streets where I was born and well-known, and on which the police were looking for the three of us. As we were wanted men we had to keep out of sight. It was just as well we had the winter nights to cover our movements. We would also have to think of finding somewhere else to stay. A lot was to happen before we could get around to doing that, and even then it was someone else who found us a place, and that was a judge at the Old Bailey.

take him away

WE HAD BEEN RUNNING AMOK all over the place, and it had to come to an end sometime, not that we thought it ever would. Our run of crime was brought to a halt in a block of flats near to Marble Arch, practically opposite to where my mother used to work in the American NAAFI. We had broken into a flat in a luxury block there. The problem for us was that we couldn't get into this flat by breaking in the front door, as it was surrounded by other flats that had people in. The only way in appeared to be through a landing window, from which we could stretch out and climb onto the balcony of the flat. So with no thought of how we would be able to get out quickly if anyone should come in, that is what we did. Once on the balcony it was easy to get into the flat. It seemed that we had been in the flat for only a few moments when John heard keys being put in the door lock. There was no point in us all charging to the balcony and trying to get out that way. Even if we could have done that, it would not have helped; our exit that way would only have fetched us onto the landing next to the front door that someone was going to come through at any moment. So we stood our ground in the hallway of the flat. Waiting for the door to open, we would then rush it as one and force our way out. The door opened alright and we charged, but there were three people coming into the flat: a lady and two men. Of course they were shocked to see the three of us charging at them from a flat where no one should have been.

As we barged into them trying to force a pathway out, they came out of their shock. The woman began screaming at the top of her voice while the men grabbed hold of us. The battle was really on then. A full-scale fight started between us all. The woman's screams brought other people from their flats, and they joined in the battle. In a way this helped us as they were getting into each other's way. The three of us were punching out, striking at anything or anyone. Eventually we broke free and headed for the internal fire stairs, leaping down them two or three at a time, a crowd of people chasing after us, all calling for us to stop. Down and down these stairs we ran until we ran out of stairs to run down. We found ourselves in the boiler house of the block of flats. As we did so we heard the slamming of a metal door behind us.

Those chasing us had locked us in the boiler house. There was no way out for us. All we could do was sit and wait for the police to come for us, which they did fairly quickly.

We were taken to Paddington Green police station where we were locked in separate cells. Later I found mine was called a detention room and not a cell. I seemed to be in this cell for hours and, bored out of my mind, I fell asleep. Finally I was woken up by a copper and taken to an interview room where my mother was sitting with a solicitor. From the moment I sat down in that room the questions came thick and fast: did I do this burglary, or this one and that one, and so on. Each time I was asked a question my solicitor told me that I need not answer, so I didn't, which pissed the copper off completely. Finally I was asked if I had committed this last burglary for which I had been arrested, and did I admit assaulting the people in that block of flats. Again I was told by my solicitor that I need not say anything, and once again I made no answer. The copper then told me that I would, with the others, be put on an identification parade for all the things I had been asked about.

The following day after a night spent in the cells, the three of us were put on these parades. I stood amongst a group of people who were supposed to look like me, but didn't, while a group of other people walked by looking at us, and as they walked by they all pointed at me. Never in a million years did I think that so many people could pick me out, but they did, and I was to find out later the same happened to John and Lee. Shortly after these identification parades were over, the three of us were charged with a string of burglaries and several assaults on people from the block of flats in which we had been arrested.

On the second morning at the police station we were taken to court, but this was a different court to the one I was used to. This one had lots of people in it who all turned to stare at us as we were ushered in. There was a public gallery at the back of the courtroom. In front of the dock were rows of benches full of solicitors, ours amongst them, and sitting high in the air behind a panelled bench sat one man - the magistrate. I was made to stand with the solicitors and my mother, while John and Lee had to stand in the dock. It appeared that as I was a juvenile I was not allowed to be put in the dock. The copper in charge stood up and told the magistrate what we were there for, and said that he wanted a remand in custody as we were absconders from an approved school, and he feared we would run away again if set loose. The magistrate agreed with the copper, but then came the problem of where to send us, me especially. The prosecutor bloke stood up and said that he did not want us sent to a remand home, as he felt sure that we would run off and commit further offences, and the charges against us now were for serious offences.

The magistrate left the court and was on the missing list for about half an hour. Eventually when he came back in he went through some talk about the serious charges and stuff like that, and the fact that we had run away from the approved school, and that he thought the only thing he could do was remand us to prison, but that he wanted the case dealt with as soon as possible. I never had time to talk to my mother. We were quickly hustled out of the courtroom, along a corridor and then locked in a cell.

Being sent to prison didn't seem to have any effect on us. During the short time in the cell we did so much mucking about; wrestling with each other and cat-calling out of the little hatch set in the door. At last we were taken out of the cells and put into a police van, and driven to Wormwood Scrubs prison.

Eventually we arrived in front of two massive wooden gates which, on the toot of the horn by the driver of the van, opened up before us. The van drove into this entrance only to be stopped by equally large gates, this time of iron bars. The wooden gates crashed to behind us while the iron ones opened in front. Driving through those, and hearing them clang to behind us, was the thing that made me now think of what I had got myself into. Once through these gates we were driven to the reception area, where we were signed for and left in the hands of the prison warders.

Within seconds of being in the reception we were locked separately into what I can only describe as cupboards. Inside these cupboards there was room to take two small steps either way. Stuck in the back wall was a plank of wood to sit on. We must have been locked in these cupboards for two to three hours. At one time we began to call out to each other, that is until a voice shouted at us, 'You three shut your fucking mouths or you will find yourself down the chokey.' What the fuck the chokey was none of us knew, and at that moment none of us wanted to find out, so we did as suggested and shut our fucking mouths! Eventually, one at a time, I heard the other two being unlocked and taken away, and not brought back. It was then that I began to feel the prison around me. It was not so much fear of the place but a sense of loneliness that came over me.

However, it was soon to be my turn to be unlocked and taken to be processed, as it was called. I followed the prison officer who had unlocked me into a large room with a large wooden table running down the centre of it. Behind that were five or six other screws (as I was to find they were called by prisoners). I was told to take all my clothes off and put them on a smaller table in front of me. As I placed each item of clothing onto the table it was picked up by one of the screws and searched. Once this was completed I was approached by one of the screws. He stood before me for some time just looking up and down my naked body. Eventually he told me to raise my hands above my head, which I did. He then ran his fingers through my hair. This finished, he walked to the back of me, then told me to spread my legs, bend over, and spread the cheeks of my arse. At this move I protested, only to have him walk back in front of me and going red in the face start to shout, 'You call me sir, you little bastard, and don't ever fucking speak until you are spoken to. Now bend over and spread the cheeks of your arse.'

Having finished that little chat, he decided to give me a smack in the face. So, bending down, I thought to myself well, if that's what grabs him, looking up boys' arses, then let him. Back behind me I could see him through my legs from my bent position, looking up my arse. It's at times like this that I wished I could fart to order! God knows what he thought he would find up my arse, but there we are, each to his own. I was to find out later that John and Lee had had the same treatment.

After I had been processed I was given my clothes back and told that as I was a remand prisoner I could wear my own gear, but that it was my reponsibility and I had to sign a paper to that effect. Still naked, and with my clothes draped over my arms, I was taken along a short corridor and into a bathroom and told to get in the bath, and not be long about it. I stepped into the four inches of water that was allowed, but before I could settle into it I was being shouted at to get out and get dressed as quick as I could, if not quicker, or I would find myself in trouble. Perhaps it was just as well I only had my feet to dry.

Now it was back to one of the cupboards for another couple of hours, but in a different part of the reception. These little cupboards seemed to be dotted around all over the place. The last thing I had to go through on this, my first night, was a medical, which thankfully took no more than about a minute. The doctor asked if I had any serious illnesses. On being told 'no' it was, 'Right, get out.'

Finally I met up with John and Lee again. We were taken to be given a bedroll, and taken to the wing of the prison we were to be kept in. The excitement of seeing each other again got us all talking at once, that is until the roar went up from the screw escorting us: 'Shut your fucking mouths! No talking until exercise.' For some reason that phrase of 'Shut your fucking mouth' seemed to be a favourite of all the screws. It could be heard from one of their mouths nearly every part of the day. There was one consolation for the three of us, we were at least going to be in the same wing and not split up altogether. Each of us was given a cell of our own.

My first night in prison had no effect on me other than to make me feel very tired, and I was soon asleep. The following morning, after a breakfast of bread and marge, a bowl of porridge and a pint mug of tea, I was taken down to see the reception committee of assistant governor, chaplain and welfare officer. There I was told what I was there for (as if I didn't know) and that was that, except for the fact that according to this mob, I had been given a number in the reception the night before. For the life of me I couldn't remember that. Now this reception committee had asked my number, and I had asked back what number? Only to be told that I was thick and I had better find out what it was or I would find myself on report. I left the assistant governor smiling, along with the chaplain and the welfare officer, over how stupid some of these prisoners were, and no wonder they were in prison. In my mind, as I left them sitting there, I just thought, 'Bollocks to you! You have me in here but that's all.' As for the screws, well, not once did I hear them call each other anything other than sir (as we prisoners had to address them) or as mister. There didn't seem to be any such thing as normal workmates in the way of calling one another Fred or Charlie or whatever. This mob were a different breed of people.

The cells were ok, as far as they could be, but it could lead to trouble if you got into bed before eight o'clock, even on a freezing winter's night. The antique heating system would be going full blast everywhere but in the cells. The bed was made of three planks of wood nailed together, and raised from the floor by blocks of wood nailed to the planks, by about four inches. Which helped the mice, they not having too far to climb to make themselves comfortable in bed. Believe me, it was not out of the ordinary to be woken up by a mouse running over your nut. Mice I could stand, in fact they were good company at night, as when having nothing to do after having read your ration of two books a week, it was good to watch the mice play. But the thing I could not stand were cockroaches. There were thousands of those bastards about. By the dim glow of light shining through the window they could be seen scuttling about. If we could only turn the light on they would run off to their dark corners, but there was no switch in the cells. All lights were turned out at nine o'clock by the night staff.

Here I was at fifteen plus and still being ruled by the regime of lights out at weird times. Laying there in darkness for hours on end was what got to me most. All that I could do was lie there and think. It is ok to turn lights out when tired, but not when you are wide awake with nothing to do but think and brood. Being on remand I was not allowed to go to work except for one hour a day. I stayed locked in my cell for the rest of the time. Having read my quota of two books a week it was just a matter of sit and count the bricks on the wall, sing to yourself, and maybe have a conversation with yourself. At night, with nothing to do but watch the mice, I even found myself talking to them, calling them 'silly fuckers' if they fell off the table or something.

Can I go on writing about my time in prison? The answer to that is no. Prison to me has been a place that turned people into nothing. But I still had to go to court.

I had made several appearances at the Magistrates Court with John and Lee, and had been sent for trial to the Old Bailey. I'd been interviewed by a barrister who was to represent me at court. His advice to me was to plead guilty to all the charges laid aginst me, John and Lee's barristers telling them the same thing. That is what we decided to do, knowing no better.

On the day of our trial we were taken to the Old Bailey by a prison bus. Driving through the streets on our way there, seeing the people on their way to work or just strolling along did make me envious for a while. But inside me there was a kind of excitement that here I was going to the highest court in the land. A court where all the top gangsters were taken, and here was I, fifteen years and seven months of age, and I was up there with them.

While waiting to go to the Bailey we had had all sorts of reports made on us, welfare and so on. Because we had been nicked for a crime of violence we had tests made on us by the doctor, like pissing in a bottle to see if we were fit enough for the birch. But as I was not yet in the right age group I could not be birched.

Waiting in the dingy cells at the Old Bailey did nothing for the three of us. There was no fear or dread as to what was going to happen to us. Not even as we read the names and sentences that had been written on the walls: Phil Reynolds - 7 years for armed robbery, John Smith - 5 years for GBH, and so on. We were even skylarking about so much that at one time one of the screws came down and with the usual, 'Shut your fucking mouths!' told us to keep quiet or he would split us up. It was the latter threat that kept us quiet. I had a confidence about me that told me that I was going to be alright, that nothing much could happen to me. I was a juvenile, the worse that could happen is that I would be sent back to an approved school from which I would run away again, and get back to my life as a burglar. But I was in for a rude awakening.

Suddenly our cell door was opened and there stood a screw saying, 'Come on you three. You're on.' We were taken along a dimly lit corridor and up a few stairs, at the top of which we were told to wait.

After five minutes or so, from above us a voice called out, 'Put up Ronald Piper, John Smith, Lee Philips.' Taking a few steps we found ourselves in the dock of the Number One Court at the Old Bailey. What a sight that was. Sitting on benches below us were our barristers in their wigs and gowns. In front of us, on a high bench, sat the judge, a grim looking old git! In front of us on the dock edges were scattered flower petals. I was told later that the purpose of them was to stop the prisoner at the bar from contaminating the court. Perhaps they thought we were all lousy and should call Nitty Nora!

The charges were read out to us by the clerk of the court and, as we had been told to do, we pleaded guilty to all of them. The prosecutor rose to his feet and then told the judge all the gory details of our life of crime. Reports were read from the probation; reports, I might add, that did nothing for us. The judge then turning to my barrister asked him if there was anything further he would like to add on my behalf. My barrister rising to his feet said, 'My Lord I have thought about this case deeply and I find there is little that I can say on this boy's behalf,' and then sat down again, the judge saying to him, 'I can understand your predicament.' John and Lee had separate barristers and they both came out with pretty much as mine had done.

Staring over his half glasses at us the judge began. 'In all the years that I have sat in this court never before have I had three such thugs as young as you before me. If I had my way you would be birched, but the law does not allow that unfortunately. You have absconded from an approved school where you were sent in the hope that it would make men of you. You, John Smith, will go to borstal training for a period of three years. You, Lee Philips, will also go to borstal for three years. As for you, Ronald Piper, you are a lot younger than the other two but to my mind that is no excuse. I cannot send you to borstal as the law states that you must be sixteen years of age before that sentence can be passed. I'm also told that you are too young to be sent to prison. But I am not going to send you back to an approved school where you can abscond from again and, I feel sure, commit other crimes. The sentence that I pass on you will be one of fifteen months imprisonment.'

So all his old chat about not being able to do this or that was a lot of old cobblers. Talking to one of the screws after we were taken to the cells, the judge having passed the usual comment, 'Take them away', it appeared that although I had been sent to prison, and the other two to borstal, in a way I had come out best. If I behaved myself I could be out free in ten months as I would get five months off for good behaviour, but John and Lee would do at least two years as that was what borstal meant at that time. So in the end I did not feel too bad, just ten months to go and I would be out.

Back in the Scrubs John and Lee were taken to a different wing to me. It seemed that borstal boys were not allowed to mix with prisoners, even those a year younger than them. A peculiar carry on, but that's the way it was. I now had ten months to serve in prison. I knew that that meant ten months of mice and cock-roaches, shitting and pissing in a chamber pot, being given hours upon hours to lay in the dark and think or brood. If I kept my 'fucking mouth shut' and obeyed all the orders, then the ten months would soon pass by, which they did. I did keep my 'fucking mouth shut', I did obey the rules or at least never got caught breaking them! For ten months I sat and sewed mailbags, not a trade that I would care to take up on the outside, but, for sixpence a week, one I did on the inside.

Since that judge and a couple of others before him passed their catch phrase on me, 'Take him away', it has been said to me on many occasions over the past forty years. As I sit at this typewriter now I am sixty two years of age, and by the time this current sentence ends I will be sixty five. Is it too late for me to change now? That I don't know. What I do know is that prison can change nothing, least of all people. It is just a containment of people who probably have been sent to prison not to rehabilitate but as a form of revenge for their deeds, and, more importantly, because no one knows anything better to do with those who transgress. Forty years or more spent in one institution or another has done nothing for me, but then I feel it was never meant to. The well-spoken phrase in itself says it all. The meaning behind it speaks for itself - Take Him Away.

80C3

ABOUT QUEENSPARK

QueenSpark is a community writing and publishing group based in Brighton. We believe that everyone has a history and that anyone who wants to can be a writer. Our aim is to encourage and publish writing by people who do not normally get into print. QueenSpark is not a commercial company. We have a part-time paid worker, but the rest of us are volunteers who work together to write and produce books, gaining and sharing skills and confidence as we go.

We have several active writing workshops in Brighton and Hove. Our manuscripts group reads all manuscripts that are sent to us and sets up book-making groups for those we are able to publish. All groups are run on a co-operative basis. If you would like to find out more or get involved, please contact us:

QueenSpark Books
Brighton Media Centre
11 Jew Street
Brighton BN1 1UT
Telephone (01273) 748348

QueenSpark is a member of the national Federation of Worker Writers and Community Publishers. We can give you the addresses of other Federation groups and information on the books they publish.

QueenSpark gratefully acknowledges the support of South East Arts, Brighton Borough Council and Hove Borough Council.